TOPOLOGICAL ANALYSIS

PRINCETON MATHEMATICAL SERIES

Editors: MARSTON MORSE and A. W. TUCKER

1. The Classical Groups, Their Invariants and Representation. By HERMANN WEYL.
2. Topological Groups. By L. PONTRJAGIN. Translated by EMMA LEHMER.
3. An Introduction to Differential Geometry with Use of the Tensor Calculus. By LUTHER PFAHLER EISENHART.
4. Dimension Theory. By WITOLD HUREWICZ and HENRY WALLMAN.
5. The Analytic Foundations of Celestial Mechanics. By AUREL WINTNER.
6. The Laplace Transform. By DAVID VERNON WIDDER.
7. Integration. By EDWARD JAMES McSHANE.
8. Theory of Lie Groups: I. By CLAUDE CHEVALLEY.
9. Mathematical Methods of Statistics. By HARALD CRAMÉR.
10. Several Complex Variables. By SALOMON BOCHNER and WILLIAM TED MARTIN.
11. Introduction to Topology. By SOLOMON LEFSCHETZ.
12. Algebraic Geometry and Topology. Edited by R. H. Fox, D. C. SPENCER, and A. W. TUCKER.
13. Algebraic Curves. By ROBERT J. WALKER.
14. The Topology of Fibre Bundles. By NORMAN STEENROD.
15. Foundations of Algebraic Topology. By SAMUEL EILENBERG and NORMAN STEENROD.
16. Functionals of Finite Riemann Surfaces. By MENAHEM SCHIFFER and DONALD C. SPENCER.
17. Introduction to Mathematical Logic, Vol. I. By ALONZO CHURCH.
18. Algebraic Geometry. By SOLOMON LEFSCHETZ.
19. Homological Algebra. By HENRI CARTAN and SAMUEL EILENBERG.
20. The Convolution Transform. By I. I. HIRSCHMAN and D. V. WIDDER.
21. Geometric Integration Theory. By HASSLER WHITNEY.
22. Qualitative Theory of Differential Equations. By V. V. NEMICKII and V. V. STEPANOV. Translated under the direction of SOLOMON LEFSCHETZ.
23. Topological Analysis. By GORDON T. WHYBURN.
24. Analytic Functions. By NEVANLINNA, BEHNKE and GRAUERT, et al.
25. Continuous Geometry. By JOHN VON NEUMANN. Foreword by ISRAEL HALPERIN.
26. Riemann Surfaces. By L. AHLFORS and L. SARIO.

TOPOLOGICAL ANALYSIS

REVISED EDITION

BY

Gordon Thomas Whyburn

PRINCETON, NEW JERSEY

PRINCETON UNIVERSITY PRESS

1964

Preface to the Second Edition

Since the publication less than five years ago of the first edition of *Topological Analysis*, outstanding developments in the field have made it desirable and necessary to rewrite the last half of the text. Happily we are now able to present some of the recently attained major goals of this area of mathematics in a satisfyingly lucid and orderly form. The principal changes have come about through the work of R. L. Plunkett, E. Connell, P. Porcelli, A. H. Read, the author and others. References to relevant recent papers will be found in the supplement to the Bibliography on page 121. A resumé and discussion of these is given in the author's paper, "Developments in topological analysis," listed in this supplement.

The role of lightness and openness has been considerably altered. These basic topological properties of mappings generated by differentiable functions are now obtained easily along the way as we prove the existence of higher derivatives, thus avoiding the difficult task of proving them at an earlier stage. At the same time the topological complexity with which one need deal has been markedly reduced. For the applications to differentiable functions, the topological index treatment could be confined to the simple case of a rectangle. Such a simplified minimal treatment of the topological index leading up to the Maximum Principle is given in the Appendix. Stoïlow's theorem in the large as well as in the small has been included, as have also the Vitali and Ascoli theorems.

G. T. WHYBURN

Charlottesville, Virginia
May, 1963

Preface to the First Edition

While the title "Topological Analysis" could embrace a wide range of subject matter, including all phases of analysis related to topology or derivable by topological methods, the material to be presented here will be centered largely around results obtainable with the aid of the circulation index of a mapping and properties resulting from openness of a mapping. This choice of topics has been governed largely by the special interests and tastes of the author, but it is hoped these may be shared to an appreciable extent by others.

Organization of some of this material was begun in 1952–1953 while the author held a Faculty Fellowship supported by the Fund for the Advancement of Education of the Ford Foundation. It was further aided by the author's participation in the University of Michigan conference on Functions of a Complex Variable in the summer of 1953, and some of the later work, especially that in Chapters V, VIII and X involving new results, was supported in part by a grant from the National Science Foundation (G 1132). The generous provision of a private study, offering freedom from interruption, by the Alderman Library of the University of Virginia during the past two sessions has greatly assisted in bringing the book to conclusion. To all of these the author takes pleasure in recording here an expression of his sincere gratitude. Thanks are due also to the editors of the Princeton Mathematical Series for their interest in the completed book and to the Princeton University Press for its careful and sympathetic handling of the task of printing and publishing it.

Charlottesville, Virginia   G. T. WHYBURN
February, 1957

Introduction

Topological analysis consists of those basic theorems of analysis, especially of the functions of a complex variable, which are essentially topological in character, developed and proved entirely by topological and pseudo-topological methods. This includes results of the analysis type, theorems about functions or mappings from one space onto another or about real or complex valued functions in particular, which are topological or pseudo-topological in character and which are obtainable largely by topological methods. Thus in a word we have analysis theorems and topological proofs. In this program a minimum use is made of all such machinery and tools of analysis as derivatives, integrals, and power series; indeed, these remain largely undefined and undeveloped.

The real objective here is the promotion, encouragement, and stimulation of the interaction between topology and analysis to the benefit of both. Certainly many new and important developments in topology, some of recent discovery, owe their origin directly to facts emerging from studies of the topological character of analytic results. Also, the opinion may be ventured that basic recent developments in analysis are due in considerable measure to the better understanding of the fundamental nature of the classical situations provided by topological concepts, results and methods. Of course, the topological character of many of the classical results of analysis has been recognized since Riemann and Poincaré, and even before them. Indeed, the very fact of this character and its recognition is in large part responsible for the origins and developments of the field of topology itself. However, the full depth of the penetration of topological nature into analytical results was surely not realized until the fairly recent past.

Contributions of fundamental concepts and results in this type of work have been made during the past twenty-five years by a large number of mathematicians. Among these should be mentioned: (1) Stoïlow [1], the originator of the interior or open mapping, who early recognized lightness and openness as the two fundamental topological properties of the class of all non-constant analytic functions; (2) Eilenberg [1] and Kuratowski [1, 2] who introduced and used an exponential representation for a mapping and related it to properties of sets in a plane;

(3) Marston Morse who in his book (see Morse [1]) and in joint studies with Heins [1] and with Jenkins [1] analyzed invariance of topological indices of a function under admissible deformations of curves in the complex plane and also conjugate nets and transverse families of curves in the plane, which has greatly clarified the action of the mapping generated by an analytic function and opened the way toward admissible simplifying assumptions; (4) the Nevanlinna [1] brothers and L. Ahlfors [1] whose outstanding work on exceptional values of analytic functions led to conclusions partly topological in character which contain the suggestion of new connections with topology still awaiting devèlopment; and (5) Ursell and Eggleston [1] as well as Titus [1] and Young who have contributed elementary proofs for the lightness and openness of analytic mappings using novel methods which have stimulated considerable further effort using these methods in the same area as well as for mappings in a more general topological setting. My own work on this subject began around 1936 as a result of reading some of Stoïlow's early papers, and has been published in an extended sequence of papers spanning the interval of nearly twenty years to the present. On two occasions, however, summaries of some of my results have been given and these are to be found in Memoirs No. 1 of the American Mathematical Society series, entitled *Open mappings on locally compact spaces* and as Lecture No. 1 in the University of Michigan's recently published *Lectures on functions of a complex variable.*

The portion of topology which is used is surprisingly small and is entirely set-theoretic in character. This is developed in Chapters I–III and consists, in brief, of (1) introductory material on compact sets, continua, and locally connected continua in separable metric spaces; (2) a discussion of continuity of transformations and of the extensibility of a uniformly continuous mapping to the closure of its domain, and a proof of the basic theorem characterizing the locally connected continuum as the image of the interval under a mapping; (3) the most basic theorems of plane topology, that is, the Jordan curve theorem, the Phragmén-Brouwer theorem, and the plane-separation theorem, which permits the separation of disconnected parts of compact sets in the plane by simple closed curves. The last group, as well as much of the first two, could be largely avoided by leaning on polygonal approximations to general curves. However, it is felt that while this would effectively reduce the topological base on which the discussion rests at present, the use of arbitrary simple arcs and simple closed curves is more natural in the theory of functions of a complex variable.

The analytical background, developed in Chapter IV, comprises only the simple properties of the complex number system and the complex plane, limits and continuity of functions, and the definition of the derivative together with its representation in terms of the partial derivatives of the real and imaginary parts of the function, but nothing beyond this for the complex derivative other than differentiability of rational combinations of differentiable functions. The mean-value theorem for real functions is presupposed. Also, the definition and the simpler properties of the exponential and logarithmic function of the complex variable are introduced and used. For example, use is made of the fact that the logarithms of a complex number are distributed vertically in the plane 2π units apart and the fact that the logarithm has continuous branches, but of nothing at all about the form of the logarithm or its derivative in terms of power series. Integration is never defined.

Only a short bibliography is included, listing some of the more closely related sources from which material has been drawn. A few citations to the bibliography are made at the ends of some of the chapters. These are meant to guide the reader to other results of similar nature and also to enable him to trace the original sources of the ideas and results through references contained in the works cited. Neither the bibliography nor the citations made to it are meant to be in any sense complete nor to indicate priority of authorship or originality of ideas or results for anyone, whether cited or not.

Table of Contents

TOPOLOGICAL ANALYSIS

I. Introductory Topology

1. Operations with sets. We shall have occasion to use sets of points and sets or collections of point sets of various sorts. Capital letters $A, B, C, \cdots$ will be used to designate sets and, in general, small letters stand for points. $a \, \varepsilon \, A$ means " a is an element of the set A" or "a is a point of A" if A is a point set. $a \ non \ \varepsilon \ A$ means that a is not an element of A.

If *A and B are sets,*

$A = B$ means that every point in the set A is also a point in the set B, and conversely every point in B is also in A.

$A \subset B$—read "A is a subset of B" or "A is contained in B"—means that every point of A is a point of B.

$A \supset B$ means $B \subset A$, "A contains B." $A = B$ is equivalent to $A \subset B$ and $B \subset A$.

$A + B$ (*sum* or *union* of A and B) means the set of all points belonging either to A or to B. In general, if $[G]$ is a collection of sets $\sum G$ is the set of all points x such that x belongs to at least one element (or set) of the collection $[G]$.

$A \cdot B$ (*intersection* or *product*) means the set of all points belonging to both A and B. For any collection of sets $[G]$, ΠG is the set of all points x such that x belongs to every set of $[G]$.

$A - B$ is by definition the set of all points which belong to A but not to B.

If $[G]$ is a collection of sets, any collection of sets each of which is an element of the collection $[G]$ is called a *subcollection* of $[G]$.

Real and complex numbers and their properties will be used freely. A set or collection whose elements can be put into (1–1) correspondence with a subset of the set of all positive integers will be called *countable*, or *enumerable*. If such a correspondence is established and the elements arranged in order of ascending integers, e.g., $a_1, a_2, a_3, \cdots$, the resulting arranged set is called a *sequence*.

The empty or vacuous set is designated by Φ. Two sets A and B are said to be *disjoint* if their intersection is empty, i e., $A \cdot B = \Phi$.

2. Metric spaces. By a *metric space* is meant a class of elements, or points, in which a *distance function* or *metric* is defined, i.e., to each pair of elements x, y of S a non-negative real number $\rho(x, y)$ is associated satisfying the conditions:

(1) $\rho(x, y) = 0$ if and only if $x = y$,

(2) $\rho(x, y) = \rho(y, x)$ (symmetry),

(3) $\rho(x, y) + \rho(y, z) \geqq \rho(x, z)$ (triangle inequality).

The following examples of metric spaces are of fundamental importance.

(i) The *real number system* R in which the distance function is defined as

$$\rho(x, y) = |x - y|, \qquad x, y \; \varepsilon \; R.$$

(ii) *Euclidean n-space* R^n with the ordinary distance function

$$\rho(x, y) = \sqrt{\sum_{1}^{n} (x_i - y_i)^2}, \qquad x = (x_1, x_2, \cdots, x_n),$$

$$y = (y_1, y_2, \cdots, y_n), \qquad x_i, y_i \; \varepsilon \; R^n.$$

Hereafter we assume all our spaces are metric. For any set X and real positive number r, $V_r(X)$ denotes the set of all points p with $\rho(p, x) < r$ for some $x \; \varepsilon \; X$. The set $V_r(X)$ will be called the *spherical neighborhood* of X with radius r.

3. Open and closed sets. Limit points. A set G in a space S is said to be *open* provided that for each $x \; \varepsilon \; G$ there exists an $r > 0$ such that $V_r(x) \subset G$. A set F is said to be *closed* provided its complement $S - F$ is open.

A point p is said to be a *limit point of* a set of points X provided every open set containing p contains at least one point of X distinct from p. For any set X, by the closure $\bar{X}$ of X is meant the set consisting of X together with all of its limit points.

The following statements are easily proven and are left as exercises for the reader:

(3.1) (a) *If a set is open, its complement is closed.*

(b) *If a set is closed, its complement is open.*

(3.2) (a) *The union of any collection of open sets is open.*

(b) *The intersection of any collection of closed sets is closed.*

(3.3) (a) *The intersection of any finite number of open sets is open.*

(b) *The union of any finite number of closed sets is closed.*

(3.4) *A point p is a limit point of a set X if and only if for each $\epsilon > 0$ there exists a point $x \; \varepsilon \; X$ different from p such that $\rho(x, p) < \epsilon$.*

(3.5) *A set F is closed if and only if it contains all of its limit points, i.e., $\bar{F} = F$.*

(3.6) *The closure of any set whatever is closed, i.e., $\bar{\bar{X}} = \bar{X}$ for any set X.*

4. Separability. Countable basis. A metric space S is separable provided some countable subset $P = \sum p_i$ of S is dense in S in the sense that every point of S either belongs to P or is a limit point of P, i.e., $\bar{P} = S$. The open sets in S are said to have a *countable basis* provided there exists a sequence $R_1, R_2, \cdots$ of open sets in S such that every open set in S is the union of a subsequence of these sets R_n, in other words, if U is any open set and $x \, \varepsilon \, U$ there exists an m such that $x \, \varepsilon \, R_m \subset U$. Such a sequence $R_1, R_2, \cdots$ will be called a *basis* or a *fundamental sequence* of open sets in S.

(4.1) *Every separable metric space has a countable basis of open sets.*

Proof. Let $P = p_1 + p_2 + \cdots$ be dense in S. Then the collection $[V_r(p_n)]$ for $n = 1, 2, \cdots$ and for all rational positive numbers r is a countable collection of open sets in S and it forms a basis in S. For let $p \, \varepsilon \, G$ where G is open. Then $p \, \varepsilon \, V_{2r}(p) \subset G$ for some rational r. There exists an n such that $p_n \, \varepsilon \, V_r(p)$, and we have $p \, \varepsilon \, V_r(p_n) \subset V_{2r}(p) \subset G$.

(4.2) LINDELÖF THEOREM. *Every collection U of open sets in a separable metric space contains a countable subcollection whose union is identical with the union of all sets in the whole collection.*

Proof. For let $R_1, R_2, \cdots$ be a basis in S. Let $R_{n_1}, R_{n_2}, \cdots$ be the subsequence of all basis sets such that R_{n_i} lies in at least one element G_i of U, i.e., an R_n becomes an R_{n_i} if and only if it lies in some element of U. Then the union of all the G_i is the same as the union of all $G \, \varepsilon \, U$ because if $x \, \varepsilon \, G \, \varepsilon \, U$, there is an n such that $x \, \varepsilon \, R_n \subset G$ and hence R_n is an R_{n_i} so that $x \, \varepsilon \, R_{n_i} \subset G_i$.

5. Compact sets. Henceforth it is assumed that all spaces used are separable and metric. A set K is *compact* provided every infinite subset of K has at least one limit point in K. A set M is *conditionally compact* provided every infinite subset of M has at least one limit point (which may or may not be in M). A set L is *locally compact* provided that for each $x \, \varepsilon \, L$ there exists an open set U containing x such that $\bar{U} \cdot L$ is compact. If L is the whole space, this obviously is the same as saying that there exists a conditionally compact open set containing p.

A real valued function $f(x)$ defined on a set X in a metric space is *upper semi-continuous* (u.s.c.) at $x_0 \, \varepsilon \, X$ provided that for any $\epsilon > 0$ there exists an open set U containing x_0 such that $f(x) < f(x_0) + \epsilon$ for all $x \, \varepsilon \, U$.

(5.1) *Any real u.s.c. function on a compact set K is bounded above on K, i.e., there exists a constant M such that $f(x) < M$ for all $x \, \varepsilon \, K$.*

For if not, there exists a sequence of distinct points $x_1, x_2, x_3, \cdots$ in K such that $f(x_n) > n$ for each n. By compactness of K, $\sum_1^\infty x_n$ has at least one limit point x_0 in K. But any open set U containing x_0 contains an x_n with $f(x_n) > f(x_0) + 1$, contrary to u.s.c. of f at x_0.

(5.2) BOREL THEOREM. *A set K is compact if and only if every collection U of open sets covering K contains a finite subcollection also covering K.*

Proof. To prove the "only if" part, we note first that by (4.2) U contains a countable subcollection $G_1, G_2, G_3, \cdots$ of elements whose union contains K. For each $x \varepsilon K$, we define $f(x) = n$ where n is the least integer such that $x \varepsilon G_n$. Then f is u.s.c. on K because $x_0 \varepsilon G_n$ implies $f(x) \leqq n$ for all $x \varepsilon G_n$. Thus by (5.1) there is an integer m such that $f(x) \leqq m$ for all $x \varepsilon K$. In other words, $K \subset \sum_1^m G_n$.

For the "if" part, we suppose K non-compact. Then there exists an infinite set I of distinct points in K having no limit point in K. Then for each $x \varepsilon K$ there exists an open set G_x containing x but containing at most one point of the set I. If a finite number of sets G_x covered K, there could be only a finite number of points in I. Thus this covering property implies compactness of K.

(5.3) (a) *Every compact set is closed.*

(b) *Every closed conditionally compact set is compact.*

(c) *If X is conditionally compact, $\bar{X}$ is compact.*

The proofs of these statements are simple and are left as exercises.

(5.4) *If $K_1 \supset K_2 \supset K_3 \cdots$ is a monotone decreasing sequence of non-empty compact sets, the intersection $P = \Pi_1^\infty K_n$ of all these sets is non-empty.*

For if P is empty, the sequence of open sets $S - K_1, S - K_2, \cdots$ covers K_1. Thus by (5.2), for some n, $K_1 \subset S - K_n$, contrary to $K_n \subset K_1$.

6. Diameters and distances.
As an immediate consequence of the definition we have

(6.1) *Any distance function $\rho(x, y)$ is continuous.*

That is, for any two points a and b and any $\epsilon > 0$ there exist neighborhoods U_a and U_b of a and b, respectively, such that for $x \varepsilon U_a$, $y \varepsilon U_b$

(i) $$\left| \rho(a, b) - \rho(x, y) \right| < \epsilon.$$

To prove this we have only to take U_a and U_b so that for $x \varepsilon U_a$, $y \varepsilon U_b$

(ii) $$\rho(a, x) < \epsilon/2, \qquad \rho(b, y) < \epsilon/2.$$

This gives by the triangle inequality

$$\rho(x, y) \leqq \rho(x, a) + \rho(a, b) + \rho(b, y) < \rho(a, b) + \epsilon,$$

$$\rho(a, b) \leqq \rho(a, x) + \rho(x, y) + \rho(y, b) < \rho(x, y) + \epsilon,$$

or

$$\rho(a, b) - \epsilon < \rho(x, y) < \rho(a, b) + \epsilon,$$

which is equivalent to (i).

DEFINITIONS. By the *diameter* $\delta(N)$ of any set N is meant the least upper bound, finite or infinite, of the aggregate $[\rho(x, y)]$ where $x, y \, \varepsilon \, N$. By the *distance* $\rho(X, Y)$ *between the two sets* X *and* Y is meant the greatest lower bound of the aggregate $[\rho(x, y)]$ for $x \, \varepsilon \, X$, $y \, \varepsilon \, Y$.

Obviously $\delta(N) = \delta(\bar{N})$ and $\rho(X, Y) = \rho(\bar{Y}, \bar{X})$ for any sets N, X, Y.

(6.2) *If* N *is compact there exist points* $x, y \, \varepsilon \, N$ *such that* $\rho(x, y) = \delta(N) < \infty$.

For let (x_1, y_1), (x_2, y_2), $\cdots$ be a sequence of pairs of points of N such that $\lim \rho(x_n, y_n) = \delta(N)$, finite or infinite. Since N is compact, the sequence $x_1, x_2, x_3, \cdots$ contains a subsequence which converges to a point x in the sense that every open set containing x contains almost all points of the subsequence, i.e., all but a finite number. We may suppose the notation adjusted so that $x_n \to x$. Similarly the sequence $[y_n]$, after the adjustment for $[x_n]$ has been made, contains a subsequence converging to a point y. Again we can adjust the notation so that $x_n \to x$, $y_n \to y$. Since $\lim \rho(x_n, y_n) = \delta(N)$, it results from (6.1) that $\rho(x, y) = \delta(N) < \infty$.

(6.3) *If* X *and* Y *are disjoint compact sets, there exist points* $x \, \varepsilon \, X$ *and* $y \, \varepsilon \, Y$ *such that*

$$\rho(x, y) = \rho(X, Y) > 0.$$

To prove this we choose a sequence of pairs of points $[(x_n, y_n)]$ as in (6.2) so that $x_n \, \varepsilon \, X$, $y_n \, \varepsilon \, Y$, $x_n \to x \, \varepsilon \, X$, $y_n \to y \, \varepsilon \, Y$, and $\lim \rho(x_n, y_n) = \rho(X, Y)$. The continuity of ρ gives $\rho(X, Y) = \rho(x, y)$ and since $x \neq y$, $\rho(x, y) > 0$.

7. Superior and inferior limits. Convergence. Let G be any infinite collection of point sets, not necessarily different. The set of all points x of our space S such that every neighborhood of x contains points of infinitely many sets of G is called the *superior limit* or *limit superior* of G and is written lim sup G. The set of all points y such that every neighborhood of y contains points of all but a finite number of the sets of G is called the *inferior limit* or *limit inferior* of G and is written lim inf G. If for a given system G, lim sup $G = $ lim inf G, then the system (collection, or sequence) G is said to be *convergent* and we write lim G = lim sup G = lim inf G. Under these conditions we say that G *converges* to the limit lim G.

For example, let G be the collection of all positive integers. Then lim sup $G = $ lim inf $G = $ lim $G = \Phi$. Thus G is convergent and has a vacuous limit. Again, let G be the system of sets $[L_n]_{n=1}^{\infty}$, where L_n is the straight line interval joining the points $[(-1)^n(1 - (1/n)), 0]$

and $[(-1)^n(1 - (1/n)), 1]$. Then lim sup G is the sum of the interval from $(-1, 0)$ to $(-1, 1)$ and the one from $(1, 0)$ to $(1, 1)$, lim inf $G = \Phi$, and thus lim G does not exist.

From the definitions, we have at once for any system G

(i)   lim inf $G \subset$ lim sup G.

Furthermore, lim inf G *and* lim sup G are *always closed point sets.* For if x is a limit point of lim inf G, then any neighborhood V of x contains a point y of lim inf G; and since V is a neighborhood also of y, then V contains points of all save a finite number of the sets of G and thus x belongs to lim inf G. Similarly if x is a limit point of lim sup G, any neighborhood V of x contains a point z of lim sup G and thus V, a neighborhood of z, contains points of infinitely many of the sets of G. Therefore x belongs to lim sup G.

It is a consequence also of our definitions that any system G having a vacuous lim sup is convergent and has a vacuous limit. In this case G is necessarily a countable system, and its elements may be ordered into a sequence $A_1, A_2, A_3, \cdots$.

If G^* is any infinite subcollection of a collection G, we have at once

(ii)   lim inf $G \subset$ lim inf $G^* \subset$ lim sup $G^* \subset$ lim sup G.

Therefore if G is a convergent system, then every infinite subcollection G^* of G is convergent and has the same limit as G.

(7.1) THEOREM. *Every infinite sequence of sets contains a convergent subsequence.*

Proof. Let $[A_i]$ be any infinite sequence of sets and let us set up the following array of sequences:

$$[A_i^1] = A_1^1, \quad A_2^1, \quad A_3^1, \cdots,$$
$$[A_i^2] = A_1^2, \quad A_2^2, \quad A_3^2, \cdots,$$
$$[A_i^3] = A_1^3, \quad A_2^3, \quad A_3^3, \cdots,$$

$$\cdot \quad \cdot \quad \cdot \quad \cdot \quad \cdot \quad \cdot \quad \cdot \quad \cdot$$

In this array, the first sequence $[A_i^1]$ is identical with the given sequence $[A_i]$; and in general for each n, the sequence $[A_i^{n+1}]$ is obtained from the sequence $[A_i^n]$ in the following manner. If the sequence $[A_i^n]$ contains any infinite subsequence whose elements occur in the same order as in $[A_i^n]$ and whose limit superior has no point in the set R_n, where R_n is the nth set in the fundamental sequence of open sets $R_1, R_2, R_3, \cdots$, then we pick out one such subsequence of $[A_i^n]$ and call it $[A_i^{n+1}]$. If, on the other hand, the limit superior of every infinite subsequence of $[A_i^n]$ has a point in R_n, then we take for $[A_i^{n+1}]$ exactly the sequence $[A_i^n]$.

We shall now prove that the diagonal sequence $[A_n^n]$ in the above array is convergent. Clearly it is an infinite subsequence of $[A_i] = [A_i^1]$, since for $k \neq j$, $A_k^k \neq A_j^j$. Suppose, on the contrary, that it is not convergent and thus that there exists a point x belonging to lim sup $[A_n^n]$ but not to lim inf $[A_n^n]$. Then there exists a neighborhood V of x, which we may take $\equiv R_m$ for some m, and an infinite subsequence $[A_{n_i}^n]$ of $[A_n^n]$ all elements of which are contained in the complement of R_m. Now the sequence $[A_n^n]$ for $n > m$ is an infinite subsequence of $[A_i^m]$ and therefore so also is $[A_{n_i}^n]$ for $i > m$. Thus $[A_i^m]$ does contain an infinite subsequence, namely $[A_{n_i}^n]$, $i > m$, whose limit superior has no point in R_m. Therefore by the method of choice of $[A_i^{n+1}]$, lim sup $[A_i^{m+1}] \cdot R_m = \Phi$. But $[A_n^n]$, for $n > m$, is a subsequence of $[A_i^{m+1}]$ and hence lim sup $[A_n^n] \cdot R_m = \Phi$, which is absurd since x belongs to both R_m and lim sup $[A_n^n]$. Thus the supposition that the sequence $[A_n^n]$ is not convergent leads to a contradiction.

(7.2) THEOREM. *If $[A_i]$ is a sequence of sets whose limit superior is L and the sum of whose elements is a conditionally compact set, then for each $\epsilon > 0$ there exists an m such that for every $n > m$, $A_n \subset V_\epsilon(L)$.*

Proof. Suppose this is not so. Then there exists an $\epsilon > 0$ and an infinite sequence of points $p_1, p_2, p_3, \cdots$ such that for each i, p_i belongs to A_{n_i} but not to $V_\epsilon(L)$ and such that $n_i \neq n_j$ for $i \neq j$. But since $\sum A_i$ is conditionally compact, there exists a point p which either is a limit point of the set $p_1 + p_2 + p_3 + \cdots$ or is identical with p_i for infinitely many i's. In either case p must belong to $L = $ lim sup $[A_i]$. But clearly this is impossible, since $V_\epsilon(L)$ contains no one of the points p_i.

COROLLARY. *If $[A_i]$ is convergent and has limit L and if $\sum_1^\infty A_i$ is conditionally compact, then for each ϵ there exists an m such that for every $n > m$, $\rho(A_n, L) < \epsilon$.*

8. Connected Sets. Well-chained sets.

A set of points M is said to be *connected* provided that however it be expressed as the sum of two disjoint non-vacuous sets M_1 and M_2, at least one of these sets will contain a limit point of the other. In other words, a set M is connected if it is not the sum of two sets A and B such that $A \cdot \bar{B} = \bar{A} \cdot B = \Phi$.

Two such sets A and B are said to be *mutually separated*, i.e., two sets A and B are mutually separated provided they are mutually exclusive ($=$ disjoint) and neither of them contains a limit point of the other. Any division of a set M of the form $M = A + B$ where A and B are non-vacuous mutually separated sets is called a *separation* of M.

It follows at once from the definition that the sum of any number of connected sets whose product does not vanish is connected. Also it follows that if M is connected, so also is any set M_0 such that $M \subset M_0 \subset \overline{M}$. For if there were a separation $M_0 = A + B$, M would be wholly in A or wholly in B, since otherwise $M = M \cdot A + M \cdot B$ would be a separation of M. This is impossible, because if $M \subset A$, every point of B would be a limit point of A and similarly if $M \subset B$.

It follows from this in particular that the closure of any connected set is connected.

By a *component* of a set M is meant a maximal connected subset of M, i.e., a connected subset of M which is not contained in any other connected subset of M. Thus for any point a of M, the component of M containing a consists of a together with all points of M in connected subsets of M containing a.

If E is any set of points, any subset F of E is called a *closed subset of E* and is said to be "closed in E" or "closed relative to E" provided that no point of $E - F$ is a limit point of F. A subset O of E is called an *open subset of E* and is said to be "open in E" provided that no point of O is a limit point of $E - O$. Now it is seen at once that a connected set may be defined as a set M no proper subset of which is both open and closed in M.

For if M is not connected and $M = A + B$ is a separation, A is both open and closed in M; and on the other hand, if a proper subset X of M is both open and closed in M, $M = X + (M - X)$ is a separation of M. Also *any component of a set M is closed in M*.

DEFINITION. If a and b are points, then by an *ϵ-chain* of points joining a and b is meant a finite sequence of points.

$$a = x_1, x_2, x_3, \cdots, x_n = b$$

such that the distance between any two successive points in this sequence is less than ϵ. A set of points M is said to be *well-chained* provided that for every $\epsilon > 0$, any two points a and b can be joined by an ϵ-chain of points all lying in the set M.

(8.1) LEMMA. *If A is any subset of any set M and ϵ is any positive number, the set M_a of all points of M which can be joined to A by an ϵ-chain of points of M is both open and closed in M.*

To prove this lemma, set $M_b = M - M_a$. Then M_a cannot contain a limit point x of M_b; for if so then some point z of M_b is at a distance less than ϵ from x and if $[a = x_1, x_2, \cdots, x_n = x]$ is an ϵ-chain in M from a to x, $a \,\epsilon\, A$, clearly $[a = x_1, x_2, \cdots, x_n, z]$ is an ϵ-chain in M from a to z, contrary to the fact that z does not belong to M_a. Thus M_a is open in M. Likewise no point z of M_b is a limit point of M_a; for if so then some point x of M_a is at a distance less than ϵ from z; and if $[a = x_1, x_2, \cdots, x_n = x]$ is an ϵ-chain in M from a to x, $a \,\epsilon\, A$, then $[a = x_1, x_2, \cdots, x_n, z]$ is an ϵ-chain in M from a to z, contrary to the fact that z does not belong to M_a. Thus M_a is closed in M and the lemma is proved.

(8.2) *Every connected set is well-chained.*

Suppose on the contrary that some connected set M contains two points a and b which, for some $\epsilon > 0$, cannot be joined by an ϵ-chain of points of M. But then by the lemma the set M_a of all points which can be so joined to b is both open and closed in M, which clearly contradicts the fact that M is connected.

Now it is not true, conversely, that every well-chained set is connected. For clearly the set R of all rational points on the unit interval $(0, 1)$ is well-chained but not connected. *However, if a set K is compact and well-chained, it is connected*, a fact which will be deduced a little later from a more general proposition.

(8.3) *If N is any connected subset of a connected set M such that $M - N$ is disconnected, then for any separation $M - N = M_1 + M_2$, $M_1 + N$ and $M_2 + N$ are connected.*

For if there existed a separation $M_1 + N = A + B$, N would have to lie wholly either in A or B, say in A, since otherwise $N = N{\cdot}A + N{\cdot}B$ would be a separation of N. This would give $B \subset M_1$. Whence $M = (M_2 + A) + B$ would be a separation of M, contrary to the connectedness of M. Similarly $M_2 + N$ is connected.

9. Limit theorem. Applications.

(9.1) THEOREM. *If $[A_i]$ is an infinite sequence of sets such that (a) $\sum A_i$ is conditionally compact, (b) for each i, any pair of points of A_i can be joined in A_i by an ϵ_i-chain and $\epsilon_i \to 0$ with $1/i$, (c) $\lim \inf [A_i] \neq \Phi$, then $\lim \sup [A_i]$ is connected.*

Proof. Let $L = \lim \sup [A_i]$, $l = \lim \inf [A_i]$. Since L is closed and contained in the compact set $\overline{\sum A_i}$, it follows that L is compact. Thus if L is not connected and we have a separation $L = A + B$, A and B are compact disjoint sets at least one of which, say A, intersects l. Thus by (6.2) $\rho(A, B) = 4d > 0$. This gives

$$\rho[V_d(A), V_d(B)] > d.$$

By (7.2) there exists an integer N such that for $n > N$, $A_n \subset V_d(L) = V_d(A) + V_d(B)$; and since $l{\cdot}A \neq \Phi$ we may suppose also $A_n{\cdot}V_d(A) \neq \Phi$. Thus there exists an integer $k > N$ such that $\epsilon_k < d$, $A_k{\cdot}V_d(A) \neq \Phi \neq A_k{\cdot}V_d(B)$. Clearly this is impossible, since if x is the last point in $V_d(A)$ of an ϵ_k-chain in A_k from a point of $V_d(A)$ to a point of $V_d(B)$ and y is the successor of x, then since $y \subset V_d(B)$ we have $\rho(x, y) > d > \epsilon_k$.

(9.11) *If $[A_i]$ is a convergent sequence satisfying (a) and (b) of (9.1), $\lim [A_i]$ is connected.*

(9.12) *If* $[A_i]$ *is a sequence of connected sets satisfying* (a) *and* (c) *of* (9.1), lim sup $[A_i]$ *is connected.*

(9.2) *If two points* a *and* b *of a compact set* K *can be joined in* K *by an* ϵ-*chain for every* $\epsilon > 0$, *they lie together in the same component of* K.

Proof. For each i, let A_i be the set of all points of K which can be joined to a by an l/i chain in K. Then since $\sum A_i \subset K$, condition (a) of (9.1) is satisfied. Condition (b) is satisfied by choosing $\epsilon_i = l/i$; and since lim inf $[A_i] \supset a + b$, (c) is satisfied. Accordingly $L = \lim \sup [A_i]$ is connected. Since $a + b \subset L \subset K$, clearly our conclusion follows. It is of interest to note that as here defined the set L actually will be a component of K.

(9.21) *Every compact well-chained set is connected.*

(9.22) *Every interval of real numbers is connected.* (Hence the real number space R is connected.)

(9.3) *If* A *and* B *are disjoint closed subsets of a compact set* K *such that no component of* K *intersects both* A *and* B, *there exists a separation* $K = K_a + K_b$, *where* K_a *and* K_b *are disjoint compact sets containing* A *and* B, *respectively.*

Proof. We first show that there exists an $\epsilon > 0$ such that no ϵ-chain in K joins a point of A to a point of B. If this is not so, then for each i there exists an l/i-chain A_i in K joining a point a_i of A to a point b_i of B. Since, by (7.1), the sequence $[A_i]$ contains a convergent subsequence, there is no loss of generality in supposing the whole sequence converges. Clearly if we take $\epsilon_i = l/i$, condition (b) of (9.1) is satisfied; and since $\sum A_i \subset K$, (a) is satisfied. Accordingly, by (9.11), $L = \lim [A_i]$ is connected. But since $A_i \cdot A \supset a_i$, $A_i \cdot B \supset b_i$, and A and B are compact, we have $L \cdot A \neq \Phi \neq L \cdot B$, contrary to the hypothesis that no component of K intersects both A and B. Thus an ϵ satisfying the above statement exists.

Now let K_a be the set of all points of K which can be joined to some point of A an ϵ-chain in K and let $K_b = K - K_a$. Then $A \subset K_a$, $B \subset K_b$. By (8.1), K_a is both open and closed in K. Accordingly K_b is open and closed in K. Since K is compact, K_a and K_b are compact.

(9.4) *If* $M_1 \supset M_2 \supset M_3 \supset \cdots$ *is a monotone decreasing sequence of nonvacuous, compact connected sets,* ΠM_i *is a non-vacuous compact connected set.*

For we have only to note that under these conditions $\Pi_i^\infty M_i = \lim [M_i] = \lim \sup M_i \neq \Phi$, and $\sum M_i = M_1$. Accordingly our conclusion follows from (9.12).

10. Continua. A compact connected set will be called a *continuum*. A locally compact connected set will be called a *generalized* continuum. If G is an open set, the set $\bar{G} - G$ will be called the *boundary* or *frontier* of G and will be denoted by $Fr(G)$. Since $Fr(G) = \bar{G} \cdot (S - G)$, where S is the whole space, *the boundary of every open set is closed*.

(10.1) *If N is a generalized continuum and G is an open set such that $N \cdot G$ is non-vacuous and different from N and $N \cdot \bar{G}$ is compact, every component of $N \cdot \bar{G}$ intersects $Fr(G)$.*

For suppose some component A of $N \cdot \bar{G}$ fails to intersect $Fr(G)$. Let $K = N \cdot \bar{G}$, $B = N \cdot Fr(G)$. Since K is compact, and A and B are closed subsets of K [B is non-vacuous because otherwise we would have the separation $N = N \cdot G + N \cdot (S - \bar{G})$, where S is the entire space], we may apply (9.3) and obtain a separation $K = K_a + K_b$ where $K_a \supset A$, $K_b \supset B$. But then $K_a \subset G$, $K_b \supset N \cdot Fr(G)$. Hence $N = K_a + (K_b + N - K)$ would be a separation since K_a and K_b are compact and $\overline{N - K} \cdot \bar{G} \subset Fr(G)$. This contradicts the connectedness of N.

If the non-degenerate continuum K is a subset of a set M, then K will be called a *continuum of convergence* of M provided there exists in M a sequence of mutually exclusive continua $K_1, K_2, K_3, \cdots$ no one of which contains a point of K and which converges to K as a limit, i.e., $K \cdot \sum_1^\infty K_i = \Phi$ and $\lim [K_i] = K$.

For example, let $M = Q + \sum_1^\infty K_i$, where Q is the square with vertices $(0, 0)$, $(1, 0)$, $(1, 1)$ and $(0, 1)$ and, for each i, K_i is the straight line interval from $(1/i, 0)$ to $(1/i, 1)$ and let K be the interval from $(0, 0)$ to $(0, 1)$. Then K is a continuum of convergence of M, for $K = \lim [K_i]$. It is to be noted that this continuum M is not *locally connected*, that is, it contains points x, e.g., the point $(0, 1/2)$, in every neighborhood of which there are points of M which cannot be joined to x by a connected subset of M of diameter less than some positive number given in advance. It is in connection with the study of the property of *local connectedness* that we find the principal applications for the notion of continuum of convergence. Indeed we shall show presently that any non-locally connected continuum always has continua of convergence of a particular type.

DEFINITION. A point set M is said to be *locally connected* at a point p of M if for every $\epsilon > 0$ a $\delta > 0$ exists such that every point x of M whose distance from p is less than δ lies together with p in a connected subset of M of diameter less than ϵ; or, in other words, if for each neighborhood U of p a neighborhood V of p exists such that every point of $M \cdot V$ lies in the component of $M \cdot U$ containing p. A set M which is locally connected at every one of its points is said to be *locally connected*.

(10.2) THEOREM. *If the generalized continuum M is not locally connected at one of its points p, then there exists a spherical neighborhood R with center p and an infinite sequence of distinct components $N_1, N_2, N_3, \cdots$ of $M \cdot \bar{R}$ converging to a limit continuum N which contains p and has no point in common with any of the continua $N_1, N_2, N_3, \cdots$.*

Proof. Since M is not locally connected at p, there exists some spherical neighborhood R with center p and radius ϵ such that $M \cdot \bar{R}$ is compact and for every positive δ, $V_\delta(p)$ contains points of M which do not belong to the component C of $M \cdot \bar{R}$ containing p. Let x_1 be such a point lying in $V_{\epsilon/2}(p)$ and let C_1 be the component of $M \cdot \bar{R}$ containing x_1. Since C_1 is closed and does not contain p, there exists a point x_2 in $M \cdot V_{\epsilon/4}(p)$ which does not belong to $C_1 + C$. Let C_2 be the component of $M \cdot \bar{R}$ containing x_2. Likewise since $C_1 + C_2$ is closed and does not contain p, there exists a point x_3 in $M \cdot V_{\epsilon/8}(p)$ which does not belong to $C + C_1 + C_2$. Let C_3 be the component of $M \cdot \bar{R}$ containing x_3, and so on. Continuing this process indefinitely, we obtain a sequence $C_1, C_2, C_3, \cdots$ of distinct [since for each n, $C_n \supset x_n$ and $x_n \cdot (C_1 + C_2 + \cdots + C_{n-1}) = \Phi$] components of $M \cdot \bar{R}$ whose inferior limit contains p.

Now, by (7.1) the sequence $[C_i]$ contains a convergent subsequence $[C_{n_i}]$ with limit N which necessarily contains p. For each i, set $N_i = C_{n_i}$. Now, by § 9, N is connected and hence is a continuum. Furthermore $N \subset C$, because $N \supset p$. Therefore $N \cdot \sum_1^\infty N_i = \Phi$. This completes the proof.

(10.3) *Every set M which contains a generalized continuum which is not locally connected has a continuum of convergence.*

(10.4) *If the generalized continuum M is not locally connected at a point p, then there exists a subcontinuum H of M containing p and such that M is not locally connected at any point of H.*

For if ϵ is the radius of R and if H denotes the component of $N \cdot \overline{V_{\epsilon/2}(p)}$ containing p as in (10.2), then it is clear that M is not locally connected at any point of H, and H is a continuum containing more than one point because it contains p and by (10.1) it must contain at least one point of $Fr[V_{\epsilon/2}(p)]$.

11. Irreducible continua. Reduction theorem.

A set of points H is said to be *irreducible* with respect to a given property P provided the set H has property P but no non-empty closed proper subset of H has property P. A set M which is irreducible with respect to the property of being a continuum containing two points a and b (or more generally a closed set K) is called an *irreducible continuum from a to b* (or about K) or a *continuum irreducible between a and b*. This means, of course, that M is a continuum containing both a and b but no proper subcontinuum of M can contain both a and b. In this section we shall prove that an arbitrary continuum M contains an irreducible continuum between any two points a and b of M or, indeed, about any given closed subset K of M. This will follow easily from a general theorem known as the Brouwer Reduction Theorem, which we now proceed to establish.

A property P is said to be *inducible* (or *inductive*) provided that when each set of a monotone decreasing sequence $A_1, A_2, A_3, \cdots$ of compact sets has property P, so also does their product $A = \Pi_1^\infty A_i$. For example, the property of being non-vacuous is inducible, as was shown in (5.4). Also the property of being connected is inducible, as was proved in (9.4).

(11.1) BROUWER REDUCTION THEOREM. *If P is an inducible property, then any non-vacuous compact set K having property P contains a non-vacuous closed subset which is irreducible with respect to property P.*

Proof. Let $R_1, R_2, \cdots$ be a fundamental sequence of neighborhoods in the space. Let n_1 be the least integer such that K contains a non-vacuous closed subset A_1 having property P and not intersecting R_{n_1}. Let n_2 be the least integer greater than n_1 such that A_1 contains a closed non-vacuous subset A_2 having property P and not intersecting R_{n_2}. Similarly, let n_3 be the least integer greater than n_2 such that A_2 contains a closed non-vacuous subset A_3 having property P and not intersecting R_{n_3}, and so on. Continuing this process indefinitely we obtain an infinite monotone decreasing sequence of compact sets $A_1, A_2, A_3, \cdots$ each having property P. Now by (5.4), if A denotes ΠA_i, then A is non-vacuous and compact; and since P is inducible, it follows that A has property P. Furthermore, A is irreducible with respect to property P. For if some proper closed subset B of A had property P, there would exist an integer k such that $R_k \cdot A \neq \Phi$ but $R_k \cdot B = \Phi$. But since $R_{n_i} \cdot A = \Phi$ for all i's we have $k \neq n_i$ for all i's, whereas $R_k \cdot B = \Phi$ would give $K = n_i$ for some $i \leq k$ by the definition of the integers n_i. (*Note.* We have assumed throughout that K itself is not already irreducible relative to property P.)

(11.2) *If K is any closed subset of a continuum, M, then M contains an irreducible subcontinuum about K.*

To see this we have only to note that the property of being a subcontinuum of M containing K is inducible.

12. Locally connected sets.

It will be recalled that a set M is *locally connected* provided it is locally connected at each of its points, i.e., for each $p \, \varepsilon \, M$ and each neighborhood U of p there exists a neighborhood V of p such that $M \cdot V$ lies in a single component of $M \cdot U$ (see § 10).

A connected open subset of a set M will be called a *region* in M.

(12.1) *A set M is locally connected if and only if each component of an arbitrary open subset of M is itself open in M.*

(12.2) *A set M is locally connected if and only if each point of M is contained in arbitrarily small regions in M.*

The proofs of these propositions result at once from the definition of local connectedness and are left as exercises.

(12.3) THEOREM. *Every connected open subset (or region) of a locally connected generalized continuum is itself a locally connected generalized continuum.*

For let R be a region in a locally connected generalized continuum M and let $p \, \varepsilon \, R$. There exists a neighborhood U of p so that $M \cdot \bar{U}$ is compact and such that $M \cdot \bar{U} = R \cdot \bar{U}$. Thus R is connected and locally compact. Finally, by local connectedness of M, there exists, for any $\epsilon > 0$, a region Q in M with $p \subset Q \subset R$ and $\delta(Q) < \epsilon$. Since clearly Q is also a region in R, it follows by (12.2) that R is locally connected.

13. Property S. Uniformly locally connected sets.

A point set M is said to have *property S* provided that for each $\epsilon > 0$, M is the sum of a finite number of connected sets each of diameter less than ϵ.

(13.1) *If M has property S, it is locally connected.*

For let x be any point of M and ϵ any positive number. Let $M = M_1 + M_2 + \cdots + M_n$, where $\delta(M_i) < \varepsilon/2$. Let K be the sum of all those sets M_i which either contain x or have x for a limit point. Then clearly K is connected and $\delta(K) < \varepsilon$. Thus since x is not a limit point of $M - K$ it follows at once that M is locally connected at x.

(13.2) *If M has property S, so also does every set M_0 such that $M \subset M_0 \subset \bar{M}$.*

For let ϵ be any positive number and let $M = M_1 + M_2 + \cdots + M_n$ where M_i is connected and of diameter less than ϵ for $1 \leq i \leq n$. Then $M_0 = \bar{M}_1 \cdot M_0 + \bar{M}_2 \cdot M_0 + \cdots + \bar{M}_n \cdot M_0$ and clearly $\overline{\bar{M}_i \cdot M_0}$ is connected (since $M_i \subset \bar{M}_i \cdot M_0 \subset \bar{M}_i$) and of diameter less than ϵ.

The two facts just established yield at once the following proposition:

(13.3) *If M has property S, then every set M_0 such that $M \subset M_0 \subset \bar{M}$ is locally connected.*

DEFINITION. If N is any subset of a metric space D and ϵ is any positive number, we shall denote by $T_\epsilon(N)$ the set of all points x of D which can be joined to N by a chain of connected subsets $L_1, L_2, \cdots, L_n$ of D such that for each i, $\delta(L_i) < \epsilon/2^i$, $L_1 \cdot N \neq \Phi$, $L_n \supset x$, and any two successive sets (links) L_i and L_{i+1} have at least one common point. Such a chain will be called a chain of type T_ϵ or simply type T.

(13.4) THEOREM. *If the metric space D has property S, then every $T_\epsilon(N)$ has property S.*

For let δ be any positive number, and let us choose an integer k such that $\sum_k^\infty \epsilon/2^i < \delta/4$. Let E be the set of all points in $T_\epsilon(N)$ which can be joined to N (i.e., to points of N) by a chain of type T which has at most k links. Let us express D as the sum of a finite number of connected sets each of diameter less than $\epsilon/2^{k+1}$; and of these sets, let $Q_1, Q_2, \cdots, Q_n$ be the ones which contain at least one point of E. Then we have

$E \subset \sum_1^n Q_i$. Now for each i, $Q_i \subset T_\epsilon(N)$; for Q_i contains a point x of E, and x can be joined to N by a chain $L_1, L_2, \cdots, L_r$ of type T having k links or less; and since $\delta(Q_i) < \epsilon/2^{k+1}$, therefore $[L_1, L_2, \cdots, L_r, Q_i]$ is a chain of type T, and hence $Q_i \subset T_\epsilon(N)$. For each i $(1 \leq i \leq n)$ let W_i be the set of all points of $T_\epsilon(N)$ which can be joined to some point of Q_i by a connected subset of $T_\epsilon(N)$ of diameter less than $\delta/4$. Then for each i, W_i is a connected subset of $T_\epsilon(N)$ of diameter less than δ. It remains only to show that $T_\epsilon(N) \subset \sum_1^n W_i$. To this end let x be any point of $T_\epsilon(N)$ and let $L_1, L_2, \cdots, L_m$ be a chain of type T joining x to N. Obviously we need consider only the case in which x does not belong to E, and in this case $m > k$. Then since $L_k \subset E$, it follows that for some j, $L_k \cdot Q_j \neq \Phi$; and since $\sum_k^\infty \epsilon/2^i < \delta/4$, it follows that $\delta(\sum_k^m L_i) \leq \sum_k^m \delta(L_i) < \delta/4$. Hence $\sum_k^m L_i$ is a connected subset of $T_\epsilon(N)$ of diameter $< \delta/4$ which joins x to a point of Q_j. Therefore $x \subset W_j$, and our theorem is proved.

(13.41) COROLLARY. *Any metric space D having property S is the sum of a finite number of arbitrarily small connected subsets each having property S. Furthermore these subsets may be chosen either as open sets or as closed sets.*

For let δ be any positive number, let $\epsilon = \delta/3$, and let $D = \sum_i^n D_i$, where each D_i is connected and of diameter less than ϵ. Then, for each i, $T_\epsilon(D_i)$ is connected and of diameter less than δ and clearly $D = \sum_i^n T_\epsilon(D_i)$. Now the sets $[T_\epsilon(D_i)]$ themselves are open; and since it is true that if a set E has property S, so does every set E_0 such that $E \subset E_0 \subset \bar{E}$, it follows that the sets $[\overline{T_\epsilon(D_i)}]$ have property S, and of course they are closed.

From this corollary it follows that in any metric space having property S there exists a monotone decreasing *fine* subdivision into connected sets. In other words, we can subdivide such a space into a finite number of connected sets each having property S and being of diameter less than 1; then we can subdivide each of these sets into a finite number of connected sets of diameter less than 1/2, and so on indefinitely.

(13.42) COROLLARY. *Any point p of a metric space D having property S is contained in an arbitrarily small connected open set (region) which has property S.*

To see this we have only to take $N = p$, and then the set $T_\epsilon(p)$ is the desired region. Since $\overline{T_\epsilon(p)}$ also has property S and hence is locally connected (because any set having property S is locally connected), we have shown that p is contained in an arbitrarily small region whose closure is locally connected.

(13.43) *Every locally connected generalized continuum has property S locally, i.e., each $p \, \epsilon \, M$ is contained in an arbitrarily small region in M having property S.*

For let $p \; \varepsilon \; M$ and let $\epsilon > 0$ be chosen so that $\overline{M \cdot V_\epsilon(p)} = K$ is compact. Then $T_\epsilon(p)$ has property S. This is proved by the same argument as given for (13.4), substituting p for N and changing the first part of the third sentence to read: "By the Borel Theorem we can cover K by a finite number of regions in M each of diameter less than $\epsilon/2^{k+1}$."

DEFINITION. A set M is said to be *uniformly locally connected* if for each $\epsilon > 0$, a $\delta_\epsilon > 0$ exists such that every two points x and y of M whose distance apart is less than δ_ϵ lie together in a connected subset of M of diameter less than ϵ.

Obviously any uniformly locally connected set is also locally connected. In case the set is compact, the converse is also true, that is:

(13.5) *Every compact locally connected set M is uniformly locally connected.*

For if not then for some $\epsilon > 0$ it is true that, for every positive integer n, some two points x_n and y_n of M exist with $\rho(x_n, y_n) < 1/n$ but which lie together in no connected subset of M of diameter less than ϵ. Since M is compact, the sequence $[x_n]$ contains a convergent subsequence $[x_{n_i}]$ with limit point p in M. Clearly the sequence $[y_{n_i}]$ also converges to p, since $\rho(x_{n_i}, y_{n_i}) < 1/n_i \leq 1/i$. But since M is locally connected at p, there exists a δ such that $V_\epsilon(p)$ lies in a region R of diameter less than ϵ. And for n_i sufficiently large, $x_{n_i} + y_{n_i} \subset R$, contrary to the definition of x_{n_i} and y_{n_i}.

We proceed now to show that the property of being uniformly locally connected is stronger for conditionally compact sets than property S. In the first place it is seen at once that, for example, if C is a circle and p is a point of C, then the set $C - p$ has property S but is not uniformly locally connected. Thus there exist sets having property S but which are not uniformly locally connected.

(13.6) *Every conditionally compact and uniformly locally connected set M has property S.*

To prove this, let ϵ be any positive number, let δ be a number greater than 0 such that every two points x and y with $\rho(x, y) < \delta$ lie together in a connected subset of M of diameter less than $\epsilon/3$, and let $P = p_1 + p_2 + \cdots$ be a countable set of points dense in M (i.e., such that $\bar{P} \supset M$). For each n, let R_n be the set of all points of M which lie together with p_n in a connected subset of M of diameter less than $\epsilon/3$. Then for each n, R_n is connected and $\delta(R_n) < \epsilon$. We now show that for some k, $M = \sum_1^k R_n$. If this is not so, then an infinite sequence $[p_{n_i}]$ of the points of P exist such that for each i, p_{n_i} is not contained in $\sum_1^{n_i-1} R_n$. Since M is conditionally compact, $[p_{n_i}]$ has a limit point p. But then some two points, say p_{n_r} and $p_{n_s}(s > r)$, are such that $\rho(p_{n_r}, p_{n_s}) < \delta$ and hence $p_{n_s} \subset R_{n_r} \subset \sum_1^{n_s-1} R_n$, contrary to the definition of the sequence $[p_{n_i}]$. Therefore, for some k, $M = \sum_1^k R_n$, and hence M has property S.

From (13.1), (13.5) and (13.6) we have at once

(13.7) *In order that a continuum M be locally connected it is necessary and sufficient that it have property S.*

14. Cartesian product spaces. If X and Y are metric spaces, the cartesian product space $X \times Y$ consists of all ordered pairs (x, y) where $x \, \varepsilon \, X$, $y \, \varepsilon \, Y$ and has distance function

$$(\ddagger) \qquad \rho(p_1, p_2) = \sqrt{\rho(x_1, x_2)^2 + \rho(y_1, y_2)^2}$$

where $p_1 = (x_1, y_1)$, $p_2 = (x_2, y_2)$ are points of $X \times Y$. This clearly satisfies all conditions for a metric except the triangle inequality. That it satisfies the latter also follows easily from

(14.1) CAUCHY-SCHWARZ INEQUALITY. *Given two sets of n real numbers* $a_1, a_2, \cdots, a_n$; $b_1, b_2, \cdots, b_n$, *we have*

$$(\dagger) \qquad \sum |a_i b_i| \leq \left[\sum a_i^2 \right]^{1/2} \left[\sum b_i^2 \right]^{1/2} = \|a\| \, \|b\|.$$

For, assuming as we may that not all a_i and not all b_i are 0,

$$0 \leq \sum \left[\frac{|a_i|}{\|a\|} - \frac{|b_i|}{\|b\|} \right]^2 = 2 - \frac{2 \sum |a_i b_i|}{\|a\| \, \|b\|}.$$

Whence $\sum |a_i b_i| \leq \|a\| \, \|b\|$, as the last term is numerically ≤ 2.

(14.11) COROLLARY. *If* $a \leq b + c$, $x \leq y + z$, *where a, b, c, x, y, z are real and non-negative,*

$$(*) \qquad \sqrt{a^2 + x^2} \leq \sqrt{b^2 + y^2} + \sqrt{c^2 + z^2}$$

For $a^2 + x^2 \leq b^2 + y^2 + c^2 + z^2 + 2(bc + yz)$

$$\leq b^2 + y^2 + c^2 + z^2 + 2\sqrt{b^2 + y^2} \sqrt{c^2 + z^2} \text{ by } (\dagger)$$

Taking square roots gives (*).

Now to get the triangle inequality in $X \times Y$, we take $p_i = (x_i, y_i) \, \varepsilon$ $X \times Y$, $i = 1, 2, 3$. Then choosing $a = \rho(x_1, x_3)$ $b = \rho(x_1, x_2)$, $c = \rho(x_2, x_3)$, $x = \rho(y_1, y_3)$, $y = \rho(y_1, y_2)$, $z = \rho(y_2, y_3)$ and applying (*) gives $\rho(p_1, p_3) \leq \rho(p_1, p_2) + \rho(p_2, p_3)$, in view of ($\ddagger$). This automatically proves the triangle inequality in the Euclidean spaces R^n. In view of the convexity of these spaces and (9.22) we have also

(14.2) *The spaces R^n are connected and uniformly locally connected.*

Also, as an easy consequence of the definition ($\ddagger$), we have

(14.3) *If X and Y are compact and metric, so also is $X \times Y$.*

II. Mappings

1. Continuity. If A and B are sets, any law which assigns to each point $x \, \varepsilon \, A$ a unique point $f(x) \, \varepsilon \, B$ is called a (single-valued) *transformation* of A *into* B. If, in addition, for each point y of B there is at least one $x \, \varepsilon \, A$ such that $f(x) = y$, f is said to be a transformation of A *onto* B and we indicate this by writing $f(A) = B$. Further, if for each $y \, \varepsilon \, B$ there is one and only one $x \, \varepsilon \, A$ with $f(x) = y$, f is said to be *one-to-one*, written 1–1 or (1–1). In this case if for each $y \, \varepsilon \, B$ we set $f^{-1}(y) = x$ we have a single-valued "inverse" f^{-1} for f.

Let $f(x)$ be a transformation of A into B. For any subset A_1 of A, $f(A_1)$ denotes the set of all points $y \, \varepsilon \, B$ such that for some $x \, \varepsilon \, A_1, f(x) = y$ and is called the *image* or the *transform* of A_1 under f. For any subset B_1 of B, $f^{-1}(B_1)$ denotes the set of all $x \, \varepsilon \, A$ such that $f(x) \, \varepsilon \, B_1$ and is called the *inverse* of B_1 under f.

A transformation f of A into B is said to be *continuous* at a point $x \, \varepsilon \, A$ provided any one of the following four equivalent conditions is satisfied:

(i) For any neighborhood U of $f(x)$ there exists a neighborhood V of x such that $f(A \cdot V) \subset U$.

(ii) For any $\epsilon > 0$ a $\delta > 0$ exists such that if $p \, \varepsilon \, A$ and $\rho(p, x) < \delta$, then $\rho(f(p), f(x)) < \epsilon$.

(iii) If (x_i) is any sequence of points in A with $x_i \to x$, then $f(x_i) \to f(x)$.

(iv) If x is a limit point of a subset M of A, $f(x)$ is either a point or a limit point of $f(M)$, i.e., if $x \, \varepsilon \, \overline{M}, f(x) \, \varepsilon \, \overline{f(M)}$.

The proof that these conditions are equivalent is left as an exercise.

If $f(x)$ is continuous at all points of A_1, $A_1 \subset A$, it is said to be *continuous on* A_1. That $f(x)$ is continuous on the whole set A on which it is defined is indicated merely by the statement that "f is continuous".

If for the (1–1) transformation $f(A) = B$, both f and its inverse f^{-1} are continuous, f is called a *topological transformation* or a *homeomorphism*. If such a transformation exists for two sets A and B, these sets are said to be *homeomorphic*.

(1.1) *The image under any continuous transformation of a $\{\begin{smallmatrix} compact \\ connected \end{smallmatrix}\}$ set is $\{\begin{smallmatrix} compact \\ connected \end{smallmatrix}\}$.*

Let A be compact and let $f(A) = B$ be a mapping. If $[G]$ is any open covering of B, then $[f^{-1}(G)]$ is an open [see (1.3) below] covering of A and hence reduces to a finite covering, say $A \subset f^{-1}(G_1) + f^{-1}(G_2) + \cdots + f^{-1}(G_n)$. This gives $B \subset G_1 + G_2 + \cdots + G_n$ so that B is compact.

Now if B is not connected, $B = B_1 + B_2$ where B_1 and B_2 are disjoint and open. This gives the separation $A = f^{-1}(B_1) + f^{-1}(B_2)$ where $f^{-1}(B_1)$ and $f^{-1}(B_2)$ are disjoint and open so that A is likewise disconnected.

DEFINITION. A transformation f is said to be *uniformly continuous* on a set A provided that for any $\epsilon > 0$ a $\delta > 0$ exists such that if x and y are any two points of A with $\rho(x, y) < \delta$, $\rho(f(x), f(y)) < \epsilon$.

(1.2) *Any transformation f which is continuous on a compact set A is uniformly continuous on A.*

Suppose that f is continuous on A but not uniformly continuous. Then for some $\epsilon > 0$ there exist two sequences of points $[x_n]$ and $[y_n]$ in A such that, for each n, $\rho(x_n, y_n) < 1/n$, but $\rho[f(x_n), f(y_n)] \geqq \epsilon$; and since A is compact we can suppose them so chosen that $[x_n] \to x$ where $x \, \epsilon \, A$. But then also $[y_n] \to x$ and thus by continuity $[f(x_n)] \to f(x)$ and $[f(y_n)] \to f(x)$, so that, for n sufficiently large, $\rho[f(x_n), f(y_n)] < \epsilon$, contrary to the definition of $[x_n]$ and $[y_n]$.

(1.3) *In order that a transformation $f(A) = B$ be continuous it is necessary and sufficient that for every $\{{open \atop closed}\}$ subset K of B, $f^{-1}(K)$ be $\{{open \atop closed}\}$ in A.*

To prove the necessity, let K be any closed subset of B and let x be any limit point of $f^{-1}(K)$. Then since by continuity, $f(x)$ is a point or a limit point of K and K is closed, we have $f(x) \, \epsilon \, K$ so that $x \, \epsilon \, f^{-1}(K)$. Thus $f^{-1}(K)$ is closed.

To show the sufficiency, let us suppose the condition is satisfied but that f is not continuous at some point $x \, \epsilon \, A$. Then there exists a sequence $[x_i] \to x$ in A and some neighborhood V of $f(x)$ in B such that for infinitely many n_i's, $f(x_{n_i}) \, \epsilon \, (B - V)$. But $B - V$ is closed in B whereas $f^{-1}(B - V) \supset \sum x_{n_i}$ and thus $f^{-1}(B - V)$ is not closed since x is a limit point of it. This contradiction proves f continuous.

(1.31) *If A, B and C are sets and $f_1(A) = B$ and $f_2(B) = C$ are continuous transformations, the transformation $f(A) = f_2 f_1(A) = f_2[f_1(A)] = C$ is continuous.*

For let K be any closed subset of C. Then $f_2^{-1}(K)$ is closed in B since f_2 is continuous, and $f_1^{-1}[f_2^{-1}(K)] = f^{-1}(K)$ is closed in A since f_1 is continuous. Hence f is continuous.

(1.4) *If A is compact, f is continuous and (1–1) and $f(A) = B$, then f^{-1} is continuous and thus f is a homeomorphism sending A into B.*

Suppose, on the contrary, that f^{-1} is not continuous at some point $y \, \epsilon \, B$, where $y = f(x)$. Then there exists in B a sequence $[y_i] \to y$ and a neighborhood U of x in A such that if $y_i = f(x_i)$, then infinitely many of the points $[x_{n_i}]$ of $[x_i]$ are in $A - U$. But since A is compact, the sequence $[x_{n_i}]$ has at least one limit point z and since $z \subset A - U$, $z \neq x$; thus $f(z) \neq y$, whereas $[f(x_{n_i})] \to y$. This contradicts the continuity of f, and thus our theorem follows.

Alternate proof. We have $f^{-1}(B) = A$. Let K be any closed set in A. Then since f is (1–1) we have

$$(f^{-1})^{-1}(K) = f(K)$$

and $f(K)$ is compact by (1.1). Thus $(f^{-1})^{-1}(K)$ is closed and hence by (1.3) f^{-1} is continuous.

(1.5) *If A has property S and $f(A) = B$ is uniformly continuous, B has property S.*

For let $\epsilon > 0$ be given. By uniform continuity of f there exists a $\delta > 0$ such that any set in A of diameter less than δ maps into a set in B of diameter less than ϵ. Thus if $A = \sum_1^k A_i$ where A_i is connected and $\delta(A_i) < \delta$, we have $B = \sum_1^k f(A_i)$ where each set $f(A_i)$ is connected, by (1.1), and of diameter less than ϵ.

(1.51) *The image of a locally connected continuum under any continuous transformation is itself a locally connected continuum.*

For (1.2) gives uniform continuity in this situation. Hence this result follows from (1.5) and $[I, (13.7)]$.

2. Complete spaces. Extension of transformations.

A sequence of points $x_1, x_2, \cdots$ is called a *fundamental sequence* or a *Cauchy sequence* provided that for any $\epsilon > 0$ an integer N exists such that if $m, n > N$, $\rho(x_m, x_n) < \epsilon$.

A metric space or set D is said to be *complete* provided every fundamental sequence in D converges to a point in D. A space or set is *topologically complete* provided it is homeomorphic with some complete space.

We have immediately

(2.1) *Every compact set is complete. Every closed subset of a complete set is complete.*

Since the real number system R is complete, it results at once that *for every $n > 0$, the Euclidean n-space R^n is complete.* For if $p_1, p_2, \cdots$ is a fundamental sequence in R^n, $p_i = (x_1^i, x_2^i, \cdots, x_n^i)$, the sequences (x_1^i), $(x_2^i), \cdots, (x_n^i)$ are fundamental sequences in R. Hence they converge to limits $x_1, x_2, \cdots, x_n$, respectively, in R; and accordingly the sequence $p_1, p_2, \cdots$ converges to the point $p = (x_1, x_2, \cdots, x_n)$ in R^n.

DEFINITION. For any metric space or set X, by the *complete enclosure* $\tilde{X}$ of $\bar{X}$ will be meant the space whose points are the fundamental sequences in X, any point $x \, \varepsilon \, X$ being identified with the sequence $(x, x, x, \cdots) \, \varepsilon \, \tilde{X}$ and two fundamental sequences $(x_1, x_2, \cdots)$ and $(y_1, y_2, \cdots)$ being the same or equivalent and determine the same point provided $(x_1, y_1, x_2, y_2, \cdots)$ is a fundamental sequence, and with the distance function

$$\rho(x, y) = \lim \rho(x_n, y_n),$$

where $x = (x_1, x_2, \cdots) \, \varepsilon \, \tilde{X}, y = (y_1, y_2, \cdots) \, \varepsilon \, \tilde{X}$.

It results at once that $\tilde{X}$ is a metric space and that X is embedded in $\tilde{X}$ *isometrically*, i.e., if $x, y \, \varepsilon \, X$, then $\rho(x, y) = \rho(x^1, y^1)$ where $x^1 = (x, x, x, \cdots) \, \varepsilon \, \tilde{X}, y^1 = (y, y, y, \cdots) \, \varepsilon \, \tilde{X}$. Furthermore, X *is dense in* $\tilde{X}$, that is, any point of $\tilde{X}$ is a point or a limit point of X or, in the space $\tilde{X}$, we have $\bar{X} = \tilde{X}$. For clearly if $x = (x_1, x_2, \cdots) \, \varepsilon \, \tilde{X}$ where $x_i \, \varepsilon \, X$, we have $x = \lim x_i^1$ where $x_i^1 = (x_i, x_i, \cdots) \, \varepsilon \, \tilde{X}$, because $\rho(x, x_i^1) = \lim_{n \to \infty} \rho(x_n, x_i)$ and for n and i sufficiently large $\rho(x_n, x_i)$ is arbitrarily small by the Cauchy condition.

Finally, the *space* $\tilde{X}$ *is complete*. For let $x_1, x_2, x_3, \cdots$ be a fundamental sequence in $\tilde{X}$ where $x_n = (x_i^n)$, $x_i^n \, \varepsilon \, X$ and where $\delta(\sum_{i=1}^{\infty} x_i^n) < 1/n$. Then the sequence (x_n^n) is a fundamental sequence. For given $\epsilon > 0$, an N exists so that for $m, n > N$,

$$\rho(x_m, x_n) = \lim_{k \to \infty} \rho(x_k^m, x_k^n) < \epsilon/3.$$

Thus if N is chosen also so that $1/N < \epsilon/3$, then for $m, n > N$ we have $\rho(x_k^m, x_k^n) < \epsilon/3$ for a definite k sufficiently large. Whence

$$\rho(x_m^m, x_n^n) \leqq \rho(x_m^m, x_k^m) + \rho(x_k^m, x_k^n) + \rho(x_k^n, x_n^n) < \epsilon/3 + \epsilon/3 + \epsilon/3 = \epsilon.$$

Accordingly $p = (x_n^n)$ is a point of $\tilde{X}$. Furthermore, since $\rho(x_k, p) = \lim_{n \to \infty} \rho(x_n^k, x_n^n) < \epsilon$, we have $x_k \to p$ so that $\tilde{X}$ is complete. Thus we have proved

(2.2) THEOREM. *Any metric space X can be isometrically imbedded in a complete space $\tilde{X}$ (called the complete enclosure of X) in which X is dense.*

(2.21) *A metric space X is complete if and only if $\tilde{X} = X$.*

We next prove an extension theorem for uniformly continuous transformations.

(2.3) *If the transformation f is defined and uniformly continuous on set D and if $f(D)$ is a subset of a complete space C, the definition of f may be extended to all limit points of D in one and only one way so that the extended transformation is uniformly continuous on $\bar{D}$ and is identical with f on D.*

Proof. For each $x \, \varepsilon \, \bar{D}$ let us select from D some sequence (x_n) with $x_n \to x$, agreeing that if $x \, \varepsilon \, D$, (x_n) is simply the sequence $x, x, x, \cdots$.

Then, by uniform continuity, for any $\epsilon > 0$ an integer N exists so that for $m, n > N$, $\rho[f(x_m), f(x_n)] < \epsilon$. Accordingly, $[f(x_i)]$ is a fundamental sequence, and since C is complete, $[f(x_i)]$ converges to some point of C which we define to be $f(x)$.

Now if (y_n) is any other sequence in D with $y_n \rightarrow x$, then since the sequence $x_1, y_1, x_2, y_2, \cdots$ also converges to x, it follows in the same way that the sequence $f(x_1), f(y_1), f(x_2), f(y_2), \cdots$ converges to $f(x)$ so that surely $f(y_n) \rightarrow f(x)$. Hence $f(x)$ is independent of the particular sequence (x_n).

Now to prove uniform continuity of f on $\bar{D}$, let $\epsilon > 0$ and let $\delta > 0$ be given by the uniform continuity of f on D. Let $x, y \; \epsilon \; \bar{D}$ with $\rho(x, y) < \delta$, and let (x_i) and (y_i) be the sequences selected above for x and y, respectively. Since $x_i \rightarrow x, y_i \rightarrow y$, for n sufficiently large we have $\rho(x_n, y_n) < \delta$ and hence $\rho[f(x_n), f(y_n)] < \epsilon$. Accordingly f is uniquely determined and uniformly continuous on $\bar{D}$. (The uniqueness results at once from continuity, since D is dense in $\bar{D}$.)

3. Mapping theorems. A continuous transformation will be called a *mapping*. Whenever the term *mapping* is used, it is understood that continuity is assumed.

(3.1) THEOREM. *If E is any locally connected continuum, there exists a mapping of the interval onto E.*

Proof. Let E be expressed as the union of a finite collection G of locally connected continua each of diameter <1 and let a and b be two distinct points of E. The elements of G may be arranged into a chain

$$C : E_1^1, E_2^1, \cdots E_n^1$$

so that $a \; \epsilon \; E_1^1$, $b \; \epsilon \; E_n^1$ and $E_i \cdot E_{i+1} \neq \Phi$ for $i = 1, 2, \cdots, n - 1$. For in the first place a and b can be joined by a chain C' of sets of G such that successive links intersect. To see this we have only to note that the union F of all points $b' \; \epsilon \; E$ which are so joinable to a is the union of a subcollection of G; and since then F would intersect some additional element H of G if there were any not in F, by connectedness of E, whereas H would have to be in F since its points clearly are chainable to a, it follows that $F = E$. Thus there is a chain C' from a to b. If C' includes k links of G and $k < n$, some link H of G not in C' intersects a link E_j^1 of C'; and if we replace E_j^1 in C' by the chain E_j^1, H, E_j^1, clearly we get a chain from a to b including $k + 1$ sets of G. By repetition of this process we obtain a chain C from a to b including all sets of G as links.

Since a link of C may be repeated any desired finite number of times, we may suppose the number of links n in C is a power of 2, say $n = 2^{v_1}$.

Then we may select a chain of points

$$a = x_0^1, x_1^1, \cdots, x_{2^{v_1}}^1 = b$$

where

$$x_i^1 \; \varepsilon \; E_i^1 \cdot E_{i+1}^1 \qquad \text{for } i = 1, 2, \cdots, (2^{v_1} - 1).$$

Next for each $i = 1, 2, \cdots, 2^{v_1}$ we express E_i^1 as the union of a finite collection of locally connected continua each of diameter $< \frac{1}{2}$ and arrange these in a chain from x_{i-1}^1 to x_i^1 with successive links intersecting as before. Further we may suppose the number of links in each of these chains is a power of 2 and indeed the same power of 2, say 2^{v_2} for all i so that our chain has the form

$$E_{i \cdot 2^{v_2}}^2, \; E_{i \cdot 2^{v_2}+1}^2 + 1 \cdots, \; E_{(i+1) \cdot 2^{v_2}}^2.$$

Then if we choose a point in the intersection of each pair of successive links we obtain a chain of points

$$x_{i-1}^1 = x_{(i-1)2^{v_2}}^2, \qquad x_{(i-1)2^{v_2}+1}^2, \cdots, x_{i \cdot 2^{v_2}}^2 = x_i^1$$

Next we express the sets E_i^2, $i = 1, 2, \cdots, 2^{v_1+v_2}$, as the union of a finite collection of locally connected continua each of diameter $< 1/2^2$, arrange these in a chain of 2^{v_3} links from x_{i-1}^2 to x_i^2 and select the points x_j^3 for $(i-1) 2^{v_3} \leq j \leq i \cdot 2^{v_3}$ as before. Continue this process indefinitely. For each k we thus have a chain of points

$$a = x_0^k, x_1^k, \cdots, \qquad x_{2^{v_1} + v_2 \cdots + v_k}^k = b.$$

Now let t be any dyadic rational number on $I = (0, 1)$ and define $f(t) = x_i^k$ where $t = i/2^{v_1+ \cdots +v_k}$. Then since the points x_i^k are so chosen that $x_{i \cdot 2^{v_k}}^k = x_i^{k-1}$, it follows that $f(t)$ is independent of the particular representation of t and thus f is single valued. Further, f is uniformly continuous on the set D of dyadic rationals on I. For if $\epsilon > 0$ let k be chosen so that $1/2^k < \epsilon/2$ and let $\delta = 1/2^{v_1 + \cdots + v_k} = 1/2^v$. Then if $t_1, t_2 \; \varepsilon \; D$ and $|t_1 - t_2| < \delta$, t_1 and t_2 lie between successive values $(j-1)/2^v$, $j/2^v$, $(j+1)/2^v$ of t in D. Let us suppose t_1 lies between the first two of these values. Then $x_{j-1}^k, x_j^k \; \varepsilon \; E_j^k$ and by the method of selection of the points x_i^k and definition of f, we have $f(t_1) \; \varepsilon \; E_j^k$. Similarly $f(t_2) \; \varepsilon \; E_{j+1}^k$ if t_2 is between $j/2^v$ and $j + 1/2^v$. In any case $f(t_1)$ and $f(t_2)$ both lie in $E_j^k + E_{j+1}^k$ and as this latter set is of diameter $< \epsilon$, it follows that f is uniformly continuous on D.

Finally to obtain a mapping of I onto E we have only to extend f to I. Then $f(I) = E$ since $f(D)$ is dense in E.

DEFINITION. A mapping $f(A) = B$ is said to be *monotone* provided that each $y \; \varepsilon \; B$, $f^{-1}(y)$ is a continuum.

(3.2) THEOREM. *Any non-degenerate monotone image of an interval is homeomorphic with the interval.*

Proof. Let $f(J) = E$ be monotone, where $J = (0, 1)$ and E is non-degenerate. Let $I(1/2)$ be the closure of the interval $J - f^{-1}f(0) - f^{-1}f(1)$ and let $x(1/2)$ be its mid point. Similarly let $I(1/2^2)$ and $I(3/2^2)$ be the closures of the left and right intervals remaining on the deletion of $f^{-1}f[x(1/2)]$ from $I(1/2)$ and let $x(1/2^2)$ and $x(3/2^2)$ be their respective mid points. Likewise $I(1/2^3), I(3/2^3), I(5/2^3), I(7/2^3)$, are the closures of the intervals into which $I(1/2^2)$ and $I(3/2^2)$ are divided by removing $f^{-1}f[x(1/2^2)]$ and $f^{-1}f[x(3/2^2)]$ ordered from left to right, and so on indefinitely. In this way we define a collection of intervals $I(m/2^n)$ and their mid points $x(m/2^n)$ for all dyadic rational numbers $m/2^n$, $0 \leq m \leq 2^n$, so that the length of $I(m/2^n)$ is $\leq 1/2^{n-1}$.

Now for any dyadic rational $m/2^n$ on J we define $h(m/2^n) = f[x(m/2^n)]$. We next show that h is uniformly continuous. Let $\epsilon > 0$ be given. By uniform continuity of f there exists a $\delta > 0$ such that for any interval H in J of length $< \delta$, $f(H)$ is of diameter $< \epsilon/2$. Let n be chosen so that $1/2^{n-1} < \delta$. Then if t_1 and t_2 are points of the set D of dyadic rationals with $|t_1 - t_2| < 1/2^n$, there is at least one point $t = j/2^n$ such that for each i $(i = 1, 2)$, t is an end point of an interval T_i of the nth dyadic subdivision of J containing t_i. If S_1 and S_2 are the corresponding intervals to T_1 and T_2 in the set $I(m/2^{n+1})$, since each is of length $< \delta$ we have

$$h(t_i) + h(t) \subset f(S_i), \quad i = 1, 2, \quad \text{and} \quad \delta[f(S_1) + f(S_2)] < \epsilon$$

since $\delta[f(S_i)] < \epsilon/2$, $i = 1, 2$. Accordingly, $\rho[h(t_1), h(t_2)] < \epsilon$ and h is uniformly continuous on D.

Let h be extended continuously to $\bar{D} = J$. Then $h(J) = f(J) = E$, because for each n the union of the intervals $I(m/2^n)$ maps onto E under f, so that the images of the mid points of all these intervals for all n, i.e., the set $h(D)$, is dense in E. Finally, h is (1–1). For if x_1 and x_2 are distinct points of J, there exists a point $t = j/2^n$ between x_1 and x_2 with $h(t) \neq h(x_1)$. Then if H_1 and H_2 are the closed intervals into which J is divided by $f^{-1}h(t)$ where $x_1 \varepsilon H_1$, $f(H_1) \cdot f(H_2) = h(t)$ by monotoneity of f and thus $h(H_1) \cdot h(H_2) = h(t)$ since $h(H_i) \subset f(H_i)$ by definition of h. Accordingly $h(x_1)$ non ε $h(H_2)$ so that $h(x_1) \neq h(x_2)$. Thus $h(J) = E$ is a homeomorphism.

4. Arcwise connectedness. Accessibility. A set T homeomorphic with a straight line interval is called a *simple arc*. If a and b are the points of such an arc T which correspond to the end points of the interval under the homeomorphism, then a and b are called the end points of the simple arc T and T is said to *join* a and b. The arc T is written ab, and the set $T - (a + b)$ is written $\widehat{ab}$ or (ab).

A boundary point p of a region R is said to be *accessible* from R provided that for any $q \, \varepsilon \, R$, $R + p$ contains a simple arc pq joining p and q.

(4.1) THEOREM. *Every two points a and b of a locally connected continuum M can be joined in M by a simple arc.*

Proof. Let $f(I) = M$ be a continuous mapping of the unit interval I onto M. Let us say that a closed subset F of I has property P provided $f(F) \supset a + b$ and if (xy) is any maximal segment of $I - F$, then $f(x) = f(y)$.

Then property P is inducible. For let F_i be closed and have property P and $F_1 \supset F_2 \supset F_3 \supset \cdots$. Let $F = \Pi F_i$ and let (xy) be a maximal open segment of $I - F$. Then there exists a sequence $(x_1 y_1)$, $(x_2 y_2)$, $\cdots$ of maximal segments complementary to $F_1, F_2, \cdots$ such that $(xy) = \sum (x_i y_i)$, $x_i \to x$, $y_i \to y$. Since $f(x_i) = f(y_i)$, clearly this gives $f(x) = f(y)$.

Thus by the Brouwer Reduction Theorem, since I has property P, there exists a closed subset A of I which has property P irreducibly. We shall show that $f(A) = T$ is a simple arc in M from a to b.

To do this we note first that if $f(x) = f(y)$ for two distinct points x and y of A, then $xy \cdot A = x + y$ because clearly $A - A \cdot (\text{int. } xy)$ would have property P. Thus if we define $h(t) = f(t)$ for $t \, \varepsilon \, A$ and $h(t) = f(x) = f(y)$ for $t \, \varepsilon$ [complementary segment xy to A in I], we obtain a mapping of I onto T which is monotone because for each $p \, \varepsilon \, T$, $h^{-1}(p)$ is either a single point of A or a closed interval xy with $xy \cdot A = x + y$. Accordingly T is a simple arc from a to b by (3.2).

(4.11) COROLLARY. *Every locally connected generalized continuum L is arcwise connected.*

For if $a, b \, \varepsilon \, L$, there exists a locally connected continuum M in L containing both a and b. To see this we let M_a be the set of all points of L which lie together with a in a locally connected continuum in L. Then M_a is open by I, (13.43), since each point y of L is interior to a locally connected continuum K_y in L. Also M_a is closed since if $y \, \varepsilon \, \bar{M}_a$, K_y contains a point x of M_a and $K_y +$ [a locally connected continuum in L joining x and a] is such a continuum joining y and a.

(4.2) THEOREM. *In order that a continuum T be a simple arc from a to b where $a, b \, \varepsilon \, T$ it is necessary and sufficient that every point of $T - a - b$ separate a and b in T.*

Proof. The necessity is immediate since any simple arc is homeomorphic with an interval. To prove the sufficiency we show first that T is locally connected. If not then T contains an infinite sequence of disjoint continua K_1, K_2, K_3, $\cdots$ converging to a non-degenerate continuum K where $K \cdot K_n = \Phi$ for all n. But then let x, y and z be distinct points on K, each distinct from a and from b. One of these three points must separate the remaining two in T. For let $T = T_a(x) + T_b(x)$ be a division of T into continua where $T_a(x) \cdot T_b(x) = x$. Then if both y and z lie in a single one of these continua, say in $T_b(x)$, let $T = T_a(y) + T_b(y)$ be a similar division of T. Then if $z \, \varepsilon \, T_b(y)$, y separates x and z because $x \, \varepsilon \, T_a(x) \subset T_a(y)$; and if $z \, \varepsilon \, T_a(y)$, z separates x and y because if $T = T_a(z) + T_b(z)$ we have $x \, \varepsilon \, T_a(x) \subset T_a(z)$, $y \, \varepsilon \, T_b(y) \subset T_b(z)$. Hence one of these points, say z, separates the other two, x and y, in T. But then since $x + y \subset K$, for all n sufficiently large we have $K_n \cdot T_a(z) \neq \Phi \neq K_n \cdot T_b(z)$ so that $z \, \varepsilon \, K_n$, contrary to the fact that the K_n are disjoint. Thus T is locally connected. Then a and b can be joined by a simple arc N in T; and clearly $N = T$ since no point of $T - N$ could separate a and b in T.

(4.3) **Theorem.** *If a region R in a locally connected generalized continuum has property S, every boundary point p of R is accessible from R.*

Proof. Since for any $\epsilon > 0$ any set having property S is the union of a finite number of connected open sets having property S and being of diameter $< \epsilon$, there is a region R_1 in R of diameter < 1 having property S and having p on its boundary. Likewise in R_1 there is a region R_2 of diameter $<1/2$ having property S and having p on its boundary; and in R_2 there is a region R_3 of diameter $<1/3$, having property S and having p on its boundary and so on indefinitely. For each n let p_n be a point of R_n and let T_n be a simple arc in R_n from p_n to p_{n+1}. Then if $T = p + \sum_1^\infty T_n$, T is a locally connected continuum in $R + p$, because $\delta(R_n) \to 0$ and $\bar{R}_n \supset p + \sum_n^\infty T_i$. Thus T, and hence also $R + p$, contains a simple arc joining p_1 and p.

5. Simple closed curves. A set J is called a *simple closed curve* provided J is homeomorphic with the set consisting of the points on a circle. It results at once that *a set J is a simple closed curve if and only if J is the union of two simple arcs axb and ayb having just their end points a and b in common.* Further, if J is any simple closed curve, then for any two distinct points α and β on J, J is the union of two simple arcs $\alpha \, x \, \beta$ and $\alpha \, y \, \beta$ intersecting in just $\alpha + \beta$. The proofs for these statements are simple and are left as exercises.

III. Plane Topology

1. Jordan curve theorem. Use will be made of the geometry results that every simple polygon P in the plane separates the plane into just two regions and is the boundary of each of these regions; and also that if P meets a segment ab in a single interior point o of ab which is not a vertex of P, then ab crosses P so that P separates a and b in the plane. In this chapter all sets considered are assumed to lie in a plane π.

(1.1) *No simple arc separates the plane.*

For if an arc $\alpha\beta$ separates the plane π, then if R_1 is a component of $\pi - \alpha\beta$, Q is a component of $\pi - (R_1 + \alpha_1\beta_1)$, where α_1 and β_1 are the first and last points of $Fr(R_1)$ on $\alpha\beta$, and R is the component of $\pi - (Q + ab)$ containing R_1, where a and b are the first and last points of $Fr(Q)$ on $\alpha_1\beta_1$, then ab separates π, and Q and R and components of $\pi - ab$.

Let C_a and C_b be disjoint circles with disjoint interiors centered at a and b respectively and let x and y be points on C_a and C_b respectively so that $ax - x$ and $by - y$ lie within C_a and C_b respectively. Let C_a' and C_b' be circles with centers a and b respectively within C_a and C_b and so that $C_a' \cdot xb = C_b' \cdot ay = \Phi$. Choosing b as origin, and using polar coordinates, let $T(\theta)$ be the triangle with vertices (r, θ), $(r, \theta + 2\pi/3)$, and $(r, \theta - 2\pi/3)$ where r is the radius of C_b'. Let C_b'' be a circle, with center b, small enough that it is within $T(\theta)$ for every θ; let z be the first point of ba on C_b'' in the order b, a and let J_b be a circle with center b which is within C_b'' and such that $az \cdot J_b = \Phi$.

Since both a and b are boundary points of both R and Q, there exist broken line segments a_1b_1 and a_2b_2 in R and Q respectively such that $a_ib_i \cdot C_a' = a_i$, $a_ib_i \cdot J_b = b_i$, $i = 1, 2$. Then $a_1b_1 +$ chord a_1a_2 of $C_a' + a_2b_2$ + chord b_2b_1 of $J_b = P$ is a simple polygon not intersecting xz of ab. Now for a suitable choice of θ (indeed for all save a finite number of θ's) we have that $T(\theta) = T$ is a triangle no vertex of which is on P and which itself contains no vertex of P. Let W denote the region obtained by adding to the interior of T the complementary region I to P which contains xz and let C denote its boundary. Then C is a graph made up of a finite number of vertices and non-intersecting edges. Any vertex of C which is a vertex of either P or T is not on the other one of these sets and hence is incident to exactly two edges of C; and any vertex v of C which is a vertex of neither P nor T is on an edge e of P and edge t of T. Thus we have exactly four segments of $T + P$ meeting in v, and of these one is within T and one within I so that exactly two are on C. Thus each vertex of C is on exactly two edges of C. Hence if G denotes the graph obtained by deleting the open segment $\widehat{a_1 a_2}$ from C, G has exactly two odd vertices a_1 and a_2 and therefore these lie in the same component L of G. (*Note:* the number of odd vertices in any finite graph G must be even. Whence, the number of odd vertices on any component L of G must be even, as L itself is a graph. Accordingly if G has exactly two odd vertices, they lie in the same component of G.) Since $xb \subset W$ we have $L \cdot xb = \Phi$; and since $L \subset a_1 b_1 + T + a_2 b_2 \subset T + R + Q$ we have $L \cdot ax = \Phi$. Accordingly $L \cdot ab = \Phi$, contrary to the fact that $a_1 \, \varepsilon \, R$ and $a_2 \, \varepsilon \, Q$ and L joins a_1 and a_2. This contradiction establishes our theorem.

(1.11) Corollary. *If* Q *is any component of the complement of a simple closed curve* J *in the plane, then* $\mathrm{Fr}(Q) = J$.

For otherwise some simple arc ab on J contains $Fr(Q)$ and thus separates the plane.

Definition. Any simple closed curve containing a straight line segment will be called a *semi-polygon.*

(1.2) Auxiliary Theorem. *Any semi-polygon separates the plane* π *into exactly two regions.*

Proof. Let S be any semi-polygon containing a straight segment aob of a line L and an arc axb with $aob \cdot axb = a + b$. Let C be a circle with center o which neither contains nor encloses any point of axb, and which therefore meets S in only two points u and v of aob. Let C_1 and C_2 be the two arc segments of $C - (a + b)$. Then no broken line in $\pi - S$ joins points of both C_1 and C_2. For suppose such a line K joins a point p_1 of C_1 and a point p_2 of C_2 and lies otherwise without C. Then $K +$ the line segment $p_1 p_2$ is a polygon P meeting S in only one point, and that point is within C and hence on aob. But P separates a and b and hence must meet axb. Therefore $\pi - S$ is not connected. Now by (1.1), S must be the boundary of each component of $\pi - S$. Thus each component of $\pi - S$ must meet $C - (a + b)$ and hence must contain either C_1 or C_2. Therefore there are just two such components.

(1.3) Jordan Curve Theorem. *Every simple closed curve* J *divides the plane* π *into just two regions and is the boundary of each of these regions.*

Proof. There exists a straight line segment ab meeting J in exactly the two points a and b. Let $ax_1 b$ and $ax_2 b$ be the two arcs of J from a to b, and denote by S_1 and S_2, respectively, the semi-polygons $ab + ax_1 b$ and $ab + ax_2 b$. By (1.3), $\pi - S_1$ and $\pi - S_2$ are composed of two regions each, say $R_1 + D_1$ and $R_2 + D_2$, respectively, where $D_1 \supset ax_2 b$

and $D_2 \supset ax_1b$. Now since $\pi - (S_1 + S_2) = R_1 + R_2 + D_1 \cdot D_2$, we have $\pi - J = (R_1 + R_2 + \widehat{ab}) + D_1 \cdot D_2$; and we thus have a division of $\pi - J$ into two non-vacuous sets. $(D_1 \cdot D_2 \neq \Phi$, because $D_1 \supset x_2$ and x_2 is a boundary point of D_2). These two sets are also mutually separated. For $D_1 \cdot D_2$ is open, as is also $R_1 + R_2$; and no point of $\widehat{ab}$ is a limit point of $D_1 \cdot D_2$. For if so then there exists a straight segment po where $o \subset \widehat{ab}$ and $po - o \subset D_1 \cdot D_2$; and if C is a circle with center o and not enclosing any point of $p + J$, then C meets ab in two points u and v and each of the three sets R_1, R_2, and $D_1 \cdot D_2$ must contain components of $C - (u + v)$; but there are only two such components and hence we have $(R_1 + R_2) \cdot (D_1 \cdot D_2) \neq \Phi$, which is impossible. Therefore $D_1 \cdot D_2$ and $R_1 + R_2 + \widehat{ab}$ are mutually separated, and thus $\pi - J$ is not connected.

Finally, $D_1 \cdot D_2$ must be connected. For by (1.11) any component of $D_1 \cdot D_2$ has all of J for its boundary. Let G be one component of $D_1 \cdot D_2$. Then there exists a broken line $L = a_1b_1$ such that $L \cdot J = a_1 + b_1$, $L - (a_1 + b_1) \subset G$, and so that a_1 and b_1 belong to ax_1b of J and $aa_1 \cdot bb_1 = \Phi$. Then $L + a_1a + ab + bb_1 = S$ is a semi-polygon lying in $G + J + ab$. If H and K are the two components of $\pi - S$, then $H \cdot J \neq \Phi \neq K \cdot J$ because S contains points of both G and ab. Thus if there were a second component G_1 of $D_1 \cdot D_2$ we would have $G_1 \cdot S \neq \Phi$. Accordingly $D_1 \cdot D_2$ is connected and our theorem is proven.

DEFINITION. By a *θ-curve* will be meant a continuum which is the sum of three simple arcs axb, ayb, azb intersecting by pairs in just their end points.

As a direct consequence of (1.3) we get

(1.4) *A θ-curve separates the plane π into just three regions.*

Proof. Let $\theta = axb + ayb + azb$, $axb + ayb = J_1$, $axb + azb = J_2$, and $ayb + azb = J_3$. For each i ($i = 1, 2, 3$) let R_i be the complementary region of J_i which does not contain the segment $\theta - J_i$. Then $\pi - \theta = R_1 + R_2 + R_3$. For if, on the contrary, $D_1 \cdot D_2 \cdot D_3 \neq \Phi$, where $D_i = \pi - J_i - R_i$, then any component D of $D_1 \cdot D_2 \cdot D_3$ has interior points of all three arcs of θ on its boundary. For any point q in D can be joined to x, say, by an arc $qx \subset D_3$; and if r is the first point of axb on qx in the order q, x, we have $qr - r \subset D$ so that $r \varepsilon Fr(D)$. Now $D + x' + y'$ contains an arc $x'y'$, and $R_1 + x'' + y''$ contains an arc $x''y''$ where $x', x'' \varepsilon \widehat{axb}$, $y', y'' \varepsilon \widehat{ayb}$. Let $J = x'y' + x'x'' + x''y'' + y''y'$ and $\pi - J = U + V$ where $U \supset a$. Then V must contain a point p of J_1 since it contains points of both R_1 and $\pi - R_1$. Say $p \subset axb$. But then since $p + a \subset axb \subset J_2 = F(R_2)$, J must contain a point of R_2, contrary to the fact that $J \subset D + \theta + R_1$.

Note. If axb, ayb, azb are the *edges* and R_1, R_2, R_3 the *regions* of a θ-curve θ, and if we understand that "an edge is *on* a region" means it is on the boundary of that region and "a region is *on* an edge" means it has the edge as a part of its boundary we get at once the following dual conclusions:

(1.5) I. *Each edge of θ is on exactly two regions.*

I'. *Each region of θ is on exactly two edges.*

II. *Each pair of edges of θ is on exactly one region.*

II'. *Each pair of regions of θ is on exactly one edge.*

2. Phragmén-Brouwer Theorém. Torhorst Theorem.

It is understood throughout this section that all sets considered lie in a plane which is usually denoted by π. If K is a closed set, by a *complementary domain* of K is meant a component of the complement of K, i.e., of $\pi - K$.

(2.1) PHRAGMÉN-BROUWER THEOREM. *The boundary of every bounded complementary domain R of a closed generalized continuum N is itself a continuum.*

Proof. For $\epsilon_1 < 1$ take a hexagonal division D_1 of the plane of norm less than ϵ_1.[1] Let H_1 be the sum of all the subdivisions in D_1 lying wholly in R. Let K_1 be any component of H_1. Assuming that K_{n-1} has been constructed, let $\epsilon_n = \rho(K_{n-1}, Fr(R))$, and construct a hexagonal divison D_n of the plane of norm less than min $(\epsilon_n, 1/n)$. Let H_n be the sum of all subdivisions of D_n which lie wholly in R, and let K_n be the component of H_n containing K_{n-1}. Make this construction for all n, and let $F_n = Fr(K_n)$.

Then for each n, F_n is a simple polygon. To show this we note first that since each vertex e of D_n on F_n is on three hexagons of D_n either one or two of which are in K_n, then in any case just two edges of F_n meet at e. Hence if a_1 and a_2 are the end points of an edge $\overparen{a_1 a_2}$ of F_n, then a_1 and a_2 are joined in the graph $G = F_n - \overparen{a_1 a_2}$ by a broken line L, as they are in the same component of G, and $a_1 a_2 + L$ is a simple polygon P in F_n. As $P \subset R$ and R is bounded, N is wholly in the exterior of P. Thus P together with its interior I lies in K_n. If $K_n \neq P + I$ then some hexagon of D_n in K_n would be exterior to P but contain an edge e of P; and this is impossible as then e would be interior to K_n and thus not on F_n. Accordingly $K_n = P + I$ so that $F_n = P$.

But, by construction, for a sufficiently large n we have $H_k \subset K_n$. Thus $Fr(R) = \lim F_n$, so that $Fr(R)$ is a continuum, as was to be proved.

---

[1] That is, the plane is represented as the union of a sequence of congruent regular hexagons plus their interiors each of diameter $<\epsilon_1$, so that the intersection of any two of these is either empty or a common side of both.

(2.11) COROLLARY. *Any compact set which is the common boundary of two domains is a continuum.*

Since one of the domains D_1 and D_2, say D_2, is bounded, we have only to note that D_2 is a complementary domain of D_1.

(2.12) *If the boundary* F *of a complementary domain of a generalized continuum is bounded,* F *is a continuum.*

(2.2) TORHORST THEOREM. *The boundary* F *of every complementary domain* R *of a locally connected continuum* M *is itself a locally connected continuum.*

Proof. For if F is not locally connected, then it contains a continuum of convergence $K = \lim (K_n)$, where $K_m \cdot K_n = \Phi$, $m \neq n$, and for some $\epsilon > 0$ we have $\delta(K_n) > 8\epsilon$ for every n. Now since M is locally connected and thus has property S, we have $M = \sum_1^n M_i$, where each M_i is a locally connected continuum of diameter less than· ϵ. Now each K_n must meet each set of some pair A, B of sets (M_i) which have no common points $(A \cdot B = \Phi)$. Since there are only a finite number of disjoint pairs A, B in (M_i), it follows that for some such pair A, B of sets M_i there exist three of the sets (K_n), say K_1, K_2, K_3, each of which meets both A and B. Now take $\sigma > 0$ such that $8\sigma < \min [\rho(K_1, K_2), \rho(K_2, K_3), \rho(K_3, K_1)]$ and consider the regions $R_\sigma(K_i) = \sum R_\sigma(x)$, $x \, \epsilon \, K_i$ in M $(i = 1, 2, 3)$ $[R_\sigma(x)$ is the component of $V_\sigma(x_i) \cdot M$ containing $x]$. These clearly are disjoint and contain arcs $a_i b_i$, respectively, such that $a_i b_i \cdot A = a_i$, $a_i b_i \cdot B = b_i$ $(i = 1, 2, 3)$. The set A contains an arc $a_1 a_2$ and an arc $a_3 a$ where $a_3 a \cdot a_1 a_2 = a$ (a may be a_3) and similarly B contains an arc $b_1 b_2$ and an arc $b_3 b$ where $b_3 b \cdot b_1 b_2 = b$. Then

$$a_1 b_1 + a_2 b_2 + a_3 b_3 + a_1 a_2 + a_3 a + b_1 b_2 + b_3 a$$
$$= a x_1 b + a x_2 b + a x_3 b$$
$$= \theta, \text{ a } \theta\text{-curve,}$$

where x_i is on $a_i b_i$ and $\rho(x_i, A) > \sigma$ and $\rho(x_i, B) > \sigma$ $(i = 1, 2, 3)$. But since x_i lies in $R_\sigma(K_i)$ it can therefore be joined to some point of K_i by a region of diameter less than σ and hence not meeting $\theta - \widehat{a x_i b}$. But then if $\pi - \theta = R_1 + R_2 + R_3$, where $R_3 \supset R$, we have that $Fr(R_3)$ meets all three edges of θ, which is impossible.

(2.21) *If the boundary* B *of a complementary domain of a locally connected generalized continuum is bounded,* B *is a locally connected continuum.*

DEFINITIONS. A point p of a connected set M is *cut point* of M provided $M - p$ is not connected. A connected set having no cut point is said to be *cyclic*. A locally connected continuum containing no simple closed curve is called an *acyclic curve*.

(2.3) LEMMA. *No acyclic curve separates the plane.*

Proof. For if so, then some acyclic curve K is the common boundary of two regions R and Q. Since K is not an arc, for some $o \ \varepsilon \ K$, $K - o$ has at least three components A, B, and C. Construct $\theta = oao' + obo' + oco' \subset R + K$ with $ao \subset A + o$, $bo \subset B + o$, $co \subset C + o$, $ao' + bo' + co' \subset R + a + b + c$. Then $\pi - \theta = R_1 + R_2 + R_3$ and Q must lie in *one* of these. This is impossible because $Fr(Q) = K \supset a + b + c$.

(2.4) *If M is a cyclicly connected locally connected generalized continuum, the boundary B of any complementary domain R of M is a simple closed curve provided B is bounded.*

Proof. Since, if $B \neq M$, B separates the plane and M is cyclicly connected, it follows that in any case B contains a simple closed curve C. Then $B = C$. For, if $B - C$ contains a point p, let px be an arc in B with $(px) \cdot C = x$ and let py be an arc in $M - x$ with $(py) \cdot C = y$. Then $px + py$ contains an arc xqy, where q lies in B. Let xay and xby be the arcs of C from x to y and set $\theta = xqy + xay + xby$, $\pi - \theta = R_1 + R_2 + R_3$, where $R_1 \supset R$. But since $Fr(R) \supset q + a + b$, whereas $Fr(R_1) = $ two of the arcs xqy, xay, xby, we have a contradiction; and hence B is a simple closed curve.

(2.41) *If N is a locally connected continuum in a plane π and a and b are points of π lying in different complementary domains R_a and R_b, respectively, of N, there exists a simple closed curve J in N separating a and b in π.*

For either R_a or R_b, say R_b, is bounded. Then if $M = \bar{R}_b$, it results at once that M is a cyclic locally connected continuum. Thus the boundary J of the complementary domain of M containing a is a simple closed curve and clearly J separates a and b.

3. Plane separation theorem. Applications.

(3.1) SEPARATION THEOREM. *If A is compact, B is a closed set with $A \cdot B = T$ totally disconnected and a, b are points of $A - A \cdot B$ and $B - A \cdot B$, respectively, and ϵ is any positive number, then there exists a simple closed curve J which separates a and b and is such that $J \cdot (A + B) \subset A \cdot B$, and every point of J is at a distance less than ϵ from some point of A.*

Proof. For each point x of $A - A \cdot B$ let C_x be the circle with center x and radius less than min $[\epsilon/2, 1/2\rho(x, B)]$, and let I_x be the interior of this circle. Let H_1 be the set of all points x of A with $\rho(x, B) \geq 1$, and for each $n > 1$, let H_n be the set of all points x of A with $1/n \leq \rho(x, B) \leq 1/(n - 1)$. Since for each n, H_n is compact, it follows that for every n there exists a finite number of the sets (I_x) with centers in H_n whose sum $K_n = \sum_{i=1}^{m_n} I_{x_i}^n$ covers H_n. Set $K = \sum_1^{\infty} K_n$, and let Q be the component of K which contains a. Then Q has no cut point, for every point of Q is an inner point of a circle lying in Q. Thus $\overline{Q}$ also has no cut point. Also $Fr(Q)\cdot(A + B) \subset A\cdot B$ and $Q\cdot B = \Phi$. Furthermore $\overline{Q}$ is locally connected, since $A\cdot B$ is totally disconnected and any point p of $\overline{Q}$ not in $A\cdot B$ is a point or a limit point of only a finite number of sets (I_n) lying in Q. Thus $\overline{Q}$ is a cyclicly connected, locally connected continuum containing a in its interior and such that $\overline{Q}\cdot B \subset A\cdot B$. Let J be the boundary of the complementary domain of $\overline{Q}$ containing b. Then, by (2.4), J is a simple closed curve. Clearly J separates a and b, and since $J \subset Fr(Q)$, we have

$$J\cdot(A + B) \subset Fr(Q)\cdot(A + B) \subset A\cdot B.$$

Finally, since every point of $Fr(Q)$ is at a distance less than $\epsilon/2$ from some point of A we have the same property for J.

(3.11) COROLLARY (ZORETTI THEOREM). *If K is a component of a compact set M and ϵ is any positive number, then there exists a simple closed curve J which encloses K and is such that $J\cdot M = \Phi$, and every point of J is at a distance less than ϵ from some point of K.*

For, by [I, (9.3)], there exists a separation of M into two mutually separated sets A and B_0, where $A \supset K$, and every point of A is at a distance less than $\epsilon/2$ from some point of K. Let r be a ray emerging from some point b such that $\rho(r, K) > 2\epsilon$. Set $B = B_0 + r$, and apply (3.1) obtaining the curve J every point of which is at a distance less than $\epsilon/2$ from A. Then J cannot enclose b, since $J\cdot r = \Phi$; and every point of J is at a distance less than $\epsilon/2 + \epsilon/2 = \epsilon$ from some point of K.

DEFINITION. A point p is called a *regular* point of a set K provided that for any $\epsilon > 0$ there exists an open set U of diameter $< \epsilon$ containing p and whose boundary intersects K in only finite number of points. If for each $\epsilon > 0$ such a U can be chosen so that $Fr(U)\cdot K$ contains $\leq n$ points, p is said to be of order $\leq n$ in K. If p is of order $\leq n$ but not of order $\leq n - 1$, then p is of order n in K.

(3.2) THEOREM. *If p is a regular point of a compact set K, then for each $\epsilon > 0$ there exists a simple closed curve J enclosing p with $\delta(J) < \epsilon$ and such that $J\cdot K$ is finite and of power less than or equal to the order of p in K.*

This follows directly from (3.1) by taking $A = K\cdot\overline{U}$, $B = K\cdot(\pi - U)$.

(3.3) *If the boundary of a region R is a simple closed curve C, then R is uniformly locally connected.*

Proof. For if not, then there exists a $d > 0$ and two sequences $X: x_1, x_2, \cdots$ and $Y: y_1, y_2, \cdots$ of points in R each converging to one and the same point p of C and such that for no n do x_n and y_n lie together in any connected subset of R of diameter less than d. Take $\epsilon = d/16$. Then since p is a point of order 2 of C, by (3.2), there exists a simple closed curve J enclosing p, with $\delta(J) < \epsilon$ and $J \cdot C = a + b$, two points. Now $J - (a + b) = \overparen{axb} + \overparen{ayb}$, where $\overparen{axb}$ and $\overparen{ayb}$ are arc segments one of which, say $\overparen{axb}$, lies within C and the other without C. Now for some n, say $n = k$, x_k and y_k both lie within J. But then if $x_k u$ and $y_k v$ are arcs in R with $(x_k u) \cdot J = u$ and $(y_k v) \cdot J = v$, we have $u + v \subset \overparen{axb}$ and hence $x_k u + \overparen{axb} + y_k v$ is a connected subset of R of diameter less than d containing x_k and y_k, contrary to the definitions of X and Y.

(3.31) COROLLARY. *If p is any point on a simple closed curve C, then for each $\epsilon > 0$ there exists an arc apb of C and an arc axb such that axb is within (without) C and $\delta(apb + axb) < \epsilon$.*

(3.32) COROLLARY. *If o is any inner point of an arc aob and ϵ is any positive number, then there exists an ϵ-simple closed curve J (i.e., $\delta(J) < \epsilon$) enclosing o and meeting aob in exactly two points u and v, where we have $u \, \epsilon \, ao$, $v \, \epsilon \, ob$.*

(3.33) COROLLARY. *The interior of every simple closed curve J has property S. The exterior E of J has property S locally, (i.e., the intersection of E with the interior of a square enclosing J has property S). Whence, every point of J is accessible from both the interior and the exterior of J.*

4. Subdivisions. By a *closed 2-cell* in the plane will be meant a set consisting of a simple closed curve plus its interior. In general, any set homeomorphic with such a set will be called a *closed 2-cell* whether in a plane or not. It follows from (4.4) below that *all closed 2-cells are homeomorphic with each other*, so that a closed 2-cell could be defined as a set homeomorphic with a circle plus its interior. By a *subdivision* of a set X is meant a representation of X as a union $X = \sum X_\alpha$ of some of its subsets X_α to be specified and meeting further specified conditions.

(4.1) SUBDIVISION THEOREM. *Let A be a closed 2-cell with interior R and boundary C. For any $\epsilon > 0$ there exists a subdivision of A into a finite number of 2-cells of diameter $< \epsilon$ such that the intersection of any two is either empty, a single point or a simple arc.*

Proof. Choose points $p_1, p_2, \cdots, p_n$ on C cyclically ordered on C and such that the diameter of the arcs $p_1 p_2, p_2 p, \cdots, p_n p_1$ are all $< \epsilon/18$. Let $x_1 y_1, x_2 y_2, \cdots, x_n y_n$ be disjoint linear segments of length $< \epsilon/9$ chosen so that for $i = 1, 2, \cdots, n$, $x_i y_i \cdot C = x_i \, \epsilon \, \overparen{p_i p_{i+1}}$, $x_i y_i - x_i \subset R$.

Now by the proof of the Phragmén-Brouwer Theorem there exists a simple polygon P in R (obtained from a hexagonal subdivision H of the plane of mesh $< \epsilon/18$) whose interior I contains all the points $y_1, y_2 \cdots, y_n$

together with all points of R at a distance $> \epsilon/18$ from C. For each i, let z_i be the first point of P on $x_i y_i$ in the order x_i, y_i. Let $z_i z_{i+1}$ denote that one of the two arcs of P from z_i to z_{i+1} which together with the arcs $x_i z_i$, $x_i x_{i+1}$ and $x_{i+1} z_i$ forms a simple closed curve C_i not enclosing the other arc of P from z_i to z_{i+1}. Now since for each i, $C - x_i x_{i+1}$ and $P - z_i z_{i+1}$ lie together on the same side (outside) of the simple closed curve $C_i = x_i x_{i+1} + x_{i+1} z_{i+1} + z_{i+1} z_i + z_i x_i$ so that the points $z_1, z_2, \cdots, z_n$ are cyclically ordered on P, it follows that for each i, $\delta(C_i + I_i) < \epsilon$ where I_i is the interior of C_i. For if $x \, \varepsilon \, I_i$, x lies in a hexagon h_1 of H contained in $P + E$ where E is the exterior of P; and since $\rho(x, C) < \epsilon/18$ there exists a chain of hexagons of H: $h_1, h_2, \cdots, h_k$ such that h_j and h_{j+1} have a common side, $j = 1, 2, \cdots, k - 1$, and such that $h_k \cdot C \neq 0$ but $h_j \cdot C = 0$ for $j < k$ and $\delta[\sum_1^k h_i] < \epsilon/9$. No h_j can lie in $P + I$, because if so then $\sum_1^j h_m$ would lie in $P + I$ as it is connected and does not intersect C, whereas h_1 is in $P + E$. Hence the union Q of the interiors of the h_j together with the open segments (sides) common to two successive hexagons $h_j, h_{j+1}, j = 1, 2, \cdots, k - 1$ cannot intersect P and, since it is connected, its closure $\overline{Q} = \sum_1^k h_i$ must intersect $x_i z_i + x_{i+1} z_{i+1} + x_i x_{i+1} = K$. Since $\delta(\overline{Q} + K) < \epsilon/3$, we have $x \, \varepsilon \, V_{\epsilon/3}(x_i x_{i+1})$ for any $x \, \varepsilon \, I_i$. Whence $\delta(C_i + I_i) = \delta(I_i) < \epsilon$. Thus the hexagons of H in $P + I$ together with the cells $C_i + I_i$, $i = 1, 2, \cdots, n$ constitute the desired subdivision of A, except that possibly some hexagon of H in $P + I$ may have a non-connected intersection with $z_i z_{i+1}$ for some i. Thus for each i we further subdivide $C_i + I_i$ by taking a finite number of disjoint broken line segments in $C_i + I_i$ each having one end in $z_i z_{i+1}$ and the other in $x_i x_{i+1}$ and so that each new cell thus obtained in $C_i + I_i$ intersects P in an arc which either lies on a single edge of P or on two consecutive intersecting edges of P. These new cells together with the hexagons of H in $P + I$ now meet the intersection requirement of our theorem.

(4.11) COROLLARY. *The interior of any simple closed curve is uniformly locally connected.*

This results at once from the fact that any two cells intersecting C have an arc in common or else their intersection is empty.

Note. By replacing each z_i which is a vertex of the subdivision of $P + I$ by a point z_i' very near z_i on P and changing $x_i z_i$ to a broken segment $x_i t_i z_i'$ very near $x_i z_i$, we obtain an ϵ-subdivision of A having the property that the intersection of each pair of 2-cells is either empty or an arc segment. A subdivision of the plane or of a region of the plane having this property will be called *simple*. It will be noted that hexagonal subdivisions have this property of simplicity. Further, a subdivision of the sort described in (4.1) is simple if and only if each point p of its 1-dimensional structure G (i.e., the complex of the boundaries of all its

2-cells) is of order ≤ 3 i.e., has at most 3 segments of G meeting in p.

Now since the same procedure as in the above proof can be applied to the exterior of C, we have the

(4.2) Theorem. *Given any simple closed curve C in the plane π, any $\epsilon > 0$ and any sufficiently fine hexagonal or simple subdivision H of π, there exists a simple ϵ-subdivision H' of π whose 1-dimensional structure includes C and which is identical with H outside $V_\epsilon(C)$.*

Now let R be any elementary region in the plane π, i.e., a region bounded by a finite number of disjoint simple closed curves $C_1, C_2, \cdots, C_n$. Then if we take ϵ less than $\frac{1}{2}$ the minimum distance between any two of the C_j and take H sufficiently fine, m-fold repeated application of (4.2) yields a simple ϵ-subdivision H' of π whose 1-dimensional structure includes all the C_j, $j = 1, \cdots, m$. The cells of H' lying in $\bar{R}$ constitute a simple ϵ-subdivision of $\bar{R}$. Here we have

(4.3) Theorem. *If R is any bounded elementary region, for any $\epsilon > 0$ there exists a simple ϵ-subdivision of $\bar{R}$.*

(4.31) *Every elementary region is uniformly locally connected.*

Definition. If A and B are closed 2-cells, or bounded elementary regions, then simple subdivisions S_a and S_b of A and B respectively are said to be *isomorphic* or *similar* provided there exists a *similarity correspondence* between them. By a similarity correspondence is meant a 1-1 relationship between S_a and S_b, say $h(S_a) = h(S_b)$, which maps the graph G_a consisting of the union of the boundaries of the 2-cells of S_a topologically onto the graph G_b made up of the union of the 2-cells of S_b and, in addition, establishes a 1-1 relation between the 2-cells of S_a and those of S_b under which boundaries are preserved, that is, if C_a is a 2-cell of S_a and C_b is its correspondent under h, then h maps the boundary of C_a homeomorphically onto the boundary of C_b.

(4.4) Theorem. *If J is any simple closed curve in the plane and $h(J) = C$ is any homeomorphism of J onto a circle C, then h can be extended to give a homeomorphism of J plus its interior onto C plus its interior.*

Proof. Let R and I denote the interiors of J and C respectively. We first show

(†) *For any $\epsilon > 0$ there exist simple ϵ-subdivisions S and S' of $J + R$ and $C + I$ respectively which correspond under a similarity correspondence which coincides with h on J.*

To show this, let S_0 be a simple ϵ-subdivision of $J + R$ as given by (4.1). We next construct a similar subdivision of $C + I$. This is done by regarding S_0 as being constructed by a finite sequence of steps each consisting of the addition of a spanning arc to the previously constructed boundary graph. That is, we have the set J to begin with. Next we add a simple arc α_1 to J having just its ends on J and lying in

$J + R$; then we add an arc α_2 spanning $J + \alpha_1$, i.e. having just its ends
in $J + \alpha_1$, and lying in $J + R$, and so on. A finite sequence, say n, of
such steps can be taken in such a way that the final graph $J + \sum_1^n \alpha_i = G_0$
is identical with the union of the boundaries of the 2-cells in S_0. Now,
going over to $C + I$, let x_1 and y_1 be the ends of α_1 and let β_1 be an arc
(line segment!) in $C + I$ joining $h(x_1)$ and $h(x_2)$; and let h be extended to a
homeomorphism from $J + \alpha_1$ to $C + \beta_1$ and to a 1-1 correspondence
between the 2 regions of $R - \alpha_1$ and the two of $I - \beta_1$ preserving
boundaries. Thus if x_2 and y_2 are the ends of α_2, then $h(x_2)$ and $h(y_2)$ are
on the boundary of one region Q in $I - \beta_1$. Hence we construct,
similarly, an arc (line segment!) β_2 from $h(x_2)$ to $h(y_2)$ and lying except for
its ends in this region Q, and let h be extended to a homeomorphism
from $J + \alpha_1 + \alpha_2$ to $C + \beta_1 + \beta_2$ and to a 1-1 correspondence between
the regions of $R - \alpha_1 - \alpha_2$ and those of $I - \beta_1 - \beta_2$ preserving boundaries. Continuing in this way for n steps we obtain the desired subdivision
S_0' of $C + I$ similar to S_0.

Now since S_0' may fail to be an ϵ-subdivision, we next take a simple
ϵ-subdivision S' of $C + I$ which is obtained by adding a finite number of
arcs (line segments!) to S_0'. [This is possible by (4.1)]. Then we make
corresponding additions to the boundary graph in S_0 by the procedure
outlined above, thus obtaining a simple ϵ-subdivision S of $J + R$ which
corresponds to S' under a similarity correspondence coinciding with h
on J. This establishes (†).

To prove the theorem we note that repeated application of (†) yields
infinite sequences of subdivisions $S_1, S_2, \cdots$ and $S_1', S_2', \cdots$ of $J + R$
and $C + I$ respectively such that (1) for each n, S_n and S_n' are simple
$1/n$-subdivisions of $J + R$ and $C + I$ respectively corresponding under
a similarity correspondence which is identical with h on J and which
maps the boundary graph G_n (i.e. the union of the boundaries of the
cells of S_n) topologically onto the corresponding graph G_n' for S_n' and
(2) for each n, S_{n+1} and S_{n+1}' are refinements of S_n and S_n' respectively in
the sense that $G_{n+1} \supset G_n$ and $G_{n+1}' \supset G_n'$. Thus h is extended topologically to G_n for each n.

We next show that as thus extended, h is uniformly continuous on
$G = \sum_1^\infty G_n$. To this end let $\epsilon > 0$ be given and let us then choose n so that
$2/n < \epsilon$. With n thus fixed, let $\delta = \min \rho(A, B)$ where A and B are an
arbitrary pair of *non-intersecting* 2-cells of the subdivision S_n. Then if
$x, y \, \epsilon \, G$ and $\rho(x, y) < \delta$, x and y lie together either in a single 2-cell
A of S_n or in two intersecting 2-cells A and B of S_n. Thus by the method
of extension of h, $h(x)$ and $h(y)$ lie either in a single cell A' or in the union
of 2 intersecting cells $A' + B'$ in S_n' so that $\rho[h(x), h(y)] \leqq \delta(A' + B')$
$< 2/n < \epsilon$. Thus h is uniformly continuous on G. By the same type of

argument, h^{-1} is uniformly continuous on $G' = \sum_{1}^{\infty} G_n'$. Accordingly, since G and G' are dense in $J + R$ and $C + I$ respectively, it follows by *II*, (2.3), that h extends to a homeomorphism of $J + R$ onto $C + I$.

(4.41) COROLLARY. *A set A is a closed 2-cell if and only if it is homeomorphic with a circle plus its interior.*

(4.42) COROLLARY. *If A and B are arbitrary closed 2-cells (in a plane or not), any homeomorphism of the edge of one onto the edge of the other can be extended to a homeomorphism of A onto B.*

REFERENCES

The material in Chapters I–III is closely related to that in the first part of Whyburn [1]. The reader is referred to this book for appropriate references to the original on other related sources. See also Moore [1]. In connection with § 4 of Chapter III see also Kerékjártó [1].

IV. Complex Numbers.
Functions of a Complex Variable

1. The complex number system. We recall that we are assuming as known all usual properties of the real numbers. The real number system is adequate for many purposes (e.g., for linear measurement) but not for all, for example, for solving simple equations. The equation

$$x^2 + 1 = 0$$

has no solution in the real number system since the left hand side is positive for any real x.

Thus we are led to define a more inclusive system, called the complex number system. This is readily accomplished by using the real numbers and their properties which we assume known; and we proceed now to outline the procedure for doing this.

(a) *Definition.* A *complex number* is any ordered pair of real numbers. If a and b are real, we denote (temporarily) the complex number defined by the pair a, b by (a, b). Two such numbers (a, b) and (c, d) are equal if and only if $a = c$ and $b = d$. Note that in general the number (a, b) is different from the number (b, a). Thus $(1, 2)$ is not the same as $(2, 1)$.

If a is real, the complex number $(a, 0)$ is to be identified with the real number a. In other words every real number a automatically becomes a complex number by identifying it with the pair $(a, 0)$. Of course we must be careful in defining rules of combination of complex numbers to make sure that these agree, in case the numbers happen to be real, with the same operations already defined for real numbers.

(b) *Sum and product.* If (a, b) and (c, d) are complex numbers ($a, b, c,$ and d real), their *sum* is defined to be the complex number $(a + c, b + d)$ and their product the complex number $(ac - bd, ad + bc)$. Thus we write

$$(a, b) + (c, d) = (a + c, b + d)$$
$$(a, b)(c, d) = (ac - bd, ad + bc).$$

We note that these definitions are consistent with the same operations on real numbers. For if a and c are real, we have

$$a + c = (a, 0) + (c, 0) = (a + c, 0) = a + c$$
$$ac = (a, 0)\,(c, 0) = (ac, 0) = ac.$$

Also, already we can show that in our new number system the equation $x^2 + 1 = 0$ has the solution $x = (0, 1)$. For

$$(0, 1)^2 + 1 = (0, 1) (0, 1) + (1, 0)$$

$$= (-1, 0) + (1, 0) = (0, 0) = 0$$

Similarly we could show also that $(0, -1)$ is a solution.

(c) *The number i. The form a + ib.* The complex number $(0, 1)$ has special significance and is denoted by i. If (a, b) is *any complex* number whatever,

$$a + ib = (a, 0) + (0, 1) (b, 0) = (a, 0) + (0, b) = (a, b).$$

Thus *any complex number (a, b) is expressible in the form $a + ib$*. This form will be used in what follows in preference to the more cumbersome and formal (a, b). Any complex number of the form $(a, 0)$ or $a + i0$ is a real number; and one of the forms $(0, b)$ or $0 + ib$ is said to be *pure imaginary*. For any complex number $(a, b) = a + ib$, a and b are called the *real part* and the *imaginary part* respectively of $a + ib$. Thus if

$$\alpha = a + ib$$

we write $R(\alpha) = a$, $I(\alpha) = b$.

We note further that

$$i^2 = (0, 1)(0, 1) = (-1, 0) = -1.$$

Thus i is a square root of -1. Similarly $(0, -1)$, which will be $-i$, is also a square root of -1.

(d) *Rules of combination.* From the definition of addition and multiplication of complex numbers we obtain at once the

Commutative laws:

$$\alpha + \beta = \beta + \alpha$$

$$\alpha\beta = \beta\alpha,$$

Associative laws:

$$(\alpha + \beta) + \gamma = \alpha + (\beta + \gamma)$$

$$(\alpha\beta)\gamma = \alpha(\beta\gamma)$$

Distributive law:

$$\alpha(\beta + \gamma) = \alpha\beta + \alpha\gamma.$$

In each case, α, β and γ are arbitrary complex numbers. The proofs here are left as exercises for the reader.

(e) *Conjugates. Neutral elements and inverses.* If $z = (a, b) = a + ib$ $= a + bi$ is any complex number, the number $z = (a, -b) = a + (-b)i$ $= a - bi$ is called the *conjugate* of z. (By commutativity it is clearly immaterial whether we write $a + ib$ or $a + bi$.)

The complex numbers 0 and 1 [i.e., $(0, 0)$ and $(1, 0)$] are *neutral* elements with respect to addition and multiplication respectively, i.e., if $\alpha = a + ib$

$$\alpha + 0 = (a, b) + (0, 0) = (a, b) = \alpha$$

$$\alpha \cdot 1 = (a, b)(1, 0) = (a, b) = \alpha.$$

Also these neutral elements are unique. For if

$$\alpha + \xi = \alpha \qquad \alpha = a + ib, \qquad \xi = s + it,$$

we have

$$(a + ib) + (s + it) = (a + s) + i(b + t) = a + ib.$$

Thus

$$a + s = a, \qquad b + t = b$$

Whence

$$s = t = 0 \qquad \text{so that} \qquad \xi = 0.$$

Similarly, we show that 1 is the only complex number which is neutral with respect to multiplication by showing that for $\alpha \neq 0$, $\alpha \cdot \beta = \alpha$ implies $\beta = 1$. (Exercise for the reader.)

For any complex number $\alpha = a + bi$, the negative of α, $-\alpha$ (addition inverse) is defined to be $-a + (-b)i$; and for $\alpha \neq 0$, the reciprocal of α, $1/\alpha$ (multiplication inverse) is defined to be

$$\frac{\bar{\alpha}}{a^2 + b^2} = \frac{a + (-b)i}{a^2 + b^2}.$$

It results at once from these definitions that $\alpha + (-\alpha) = 0$ and $\alpha(1/\alpha) = 1$. Further these inverses are unique. Suppose, for example,

$$\alpha \alpha' = 1 \qquad 0 \neq \alpha = a + bi, \qquad \alpha' = a' + b'i.$$

Then $(aa' - bb') + (ab' + a'b)i = 1 = 1 + 0i$. Whence $aa' - bb' = 1$, $ab' + a'b = 0$. Solving these two equations simultaneously gives

$$a' = \frac{a}{a^2 + b^2}, \qquad b' = \frac{-b}{a^2 + b^2}.$$

We note finally that if α and β are complex numbers, $\alpha\beta = 0$ implies either $\alpha = 0$ or $\beta = 0$. For if $\alpha \neq 0$, multiplying $\alpha\beta = 0$ by $1/\alpha$ gives

$$\frac{1}{\alpha}(\alpha\beta) = \left(\frac{1}{\alpha}\alpha\right)\beta = 1\beta = \beta = \frac{1}{\alpha} 0 = 0.$$

(f) *Subtraction and division* are now defined in terms of the inverses under addition and multiplication respectively. Thus if $\alpha = a + bi$,

$\beta = c + di$ we define $\beta - \alpha$ to be $\beta + (-\alpha)$ and, for $\alpha \neq 0$, β/α to be $\beta \cdot (1/\alpha)$ so that

$$\beta - \alpha = (c - a) + (d - b)i$$

$$\frac{\beta}{\alpha} = \frac{ac + bd}{a^2 + b^2} + \frac{ad - bc}{a^2 + b^2} i \qquad\qquad \alpha \neq 0.$$

These latter numbers are readily seen to be solutions, respectively, of the equations

$$z + \alpha = \beta$$

and

$$\alpha z = \beta$$

Further, these solutions are unique. The reader should prove this.

By adding and subtracting the equations

$$\alpha = a + bi$$
$$\bar{\alpha} = a - bi$$

we get the relations

$$\alpha + \bar{\alpha} = 2a = 2R(\alpha)$$
$$\alpha - \bar{\alpha} = 2b = 2I(\alpha),$$

for the real and imaginary parts of α in terms of α and its conjugate. It is now easy also to show that every complex number has two square roots. For let

$$a + bi = (x + iy)^2 = x^2 - y^2 + 2xyi;$$

whence

$$x^2 - y^2 = a$$
$$2xy = b.$$

Solving these latter two equations simultaneously gives

$$x = \pm \sqrt{\frac{a + \sqrt{a^2 + b^2}}{2}}, \qquad y = \pm \sqrt{\frac{\sqrt{a^2 + b^2} - a}{2}}.$$

The numbers under the outer radicals are always positive or 0 so that x and y are real. However the signs must be paired so as to satisfy $2xy = b$, that is, the signs must agree if $b > 0$ and must differ if $b < 0$.

It now follows that any quadratic equation with complex coefficients has solutions given by the usual quadratic formula.

(g) *The complex plane.* It is natural to represent the complex numbers $x + yi$ by the points (x, y) in a cartesian plane, that is we make the point with coordinates (x, y) in the plane correspond to the complex number $x + yi$. When used for this purpose the plane is called a complex plane. Clearly the relationship between the points in the complex plane and the set of all complex numbers is one to one. The real numbers are represented by the points on the x-axis and the pure imaginary numbers by points on the y-axis. For this reason the x-axis in the complex plane is referred to as the *real axis* or *axis of reals* and the y-axis as the *imaginary axis*. Addition and subtraction of complex numbers when transferred to the complex plane become ordinary vector addition and subtraction where the complex number $x + iy$ is interpreted as the vector with components x and y.

(h) *The polar form.* Using polar coordinates (ρ, θ) in the complex plane, the number $x + iy$ takes the form

$$\rho(\cos \theta + i \sin \theta)$$

since

$$x = \rho \cos \theta \quad \text{and} \quad y = \rho \sin \theta.$$

This is called the *polar form* of the number $x + iy$. We have

$$\rho = \sqrt{x^2 + y^2}, \qquad \theta = \arctan \frac{y}{x}$$

and these are called the *modulus* (or absolute value) and *amplitude* respectively of $x + iy$. We shall always take ρ to be a non-negative number and will designate it also by $|x + iy|$. Thus as we use it $\rho = |z|$ has a unique value for each complex number z. The amplitude, on the other hand, is many valued. For $x = 0$, by convention we take $\theta = \pm \pi/2 + 2k\pi$, $k = 0, \pm 1, \pm 2, \cdots$, the sign in front of $\pi/2$ being chosen so as to agree with that of y for $y \neq 0$; and for both x and $y = 0$, i.e., for $x + iy = 0$, θ is not defined. Since ρ is restricted to non-negative values it is necessary to restrict also the choice of θ among the values of $\arctan y/x$. This is accomplished by taking for θ those values of $\arctan y/x$ and only those of the form $\theta_0 \pm 2k\pi$ $(k = 0, 1, 2, \cdots)$ where $0 \leq \theta_0 < 2\pi$ and where

$$\theta_0 = 0 \qquad \text{when } x > 0 \text{ and } y = 0$$

$$0 < \theta_0 < \pi/2 \qquad \text{when } x > 0 \text{ and } y > 0$$

$$\theta_0 = \pi/2 \qquad \text{when } x = 0 \text{ and } y > 0$$

$$\pi/2 < \theta_0 < \pi \qquad \text{when } x < 0 \text{ and } y > 0$$

$$\theta = \pi \qquad \text{when } x < 0 \text{ and } y = 0$$

$$\pi < \theta_0 < 3\pi/2 \qquad \text{when } x < 0 \text{ and } y < 0$$

$$\theta_0 = 3\pi/2 \qquad \text{when } x = 0 \text{ and } y < 0$$

$$3\pi/2 < \theta_0 < 2\pi \qquad \text{when } x > 0 \text{ and } y < 0.$$

It may be noted that although apparently geometric, the modulus and amplitude of a complex number can be made purely analytic concepts. This is clear for ρ; and to accomplish it for θ it is only necessary to note that the trigonometric and inverse trigonometric functions of real arguments are definable analytically either as infinite series or as definite integrals.

Multiplication and division of complex numbers is exhibited lucidly in terms of the polar forms of the numbers. For if

$$z_1 = \rho_1(\cos \theta_1 + i \sin \theta_1), \quad z_2 = \rho_2(\cos \theta_2 + i \sin \theta_2),$$

we have

$$z_1 z_2 = \rho_1 \rho_2[(\cos \theta_1 \cos \theta_2 - \sin \theta_1 \sin \theta_2) + i(\cos \theta_1 \sin \theta_2 + \sin \theta_1 \cos \theta_2)$$
$$= \rho_1 \rho_2[\cos (\theta_1 + \theta_2) + i \sin (\theta_1 + \theta_2)].$$

Similarly, for $z_2 \neq 0$,

$$\frac{z_1}{z_2} = \frac{\rho_1}{\rho_2}[\cos (\theta_1 - \theta_2) + i \sin (\theta_1 - \theta_2)].$$

Thus to multiply we multiply moduli and add the amplitudes and to divide we divide moduli and subtract the amplitude of the divisor from that of the dividend. In particular the reciprocal of a (non-zero) complex number with modulus ρ and amplitude θ is the number with modulus $1/\rho$ and amplitude $-\theta$, i.e., if $z = \rho(\cos \theta + i \sin \theta)$ we have

$$\frac{1}{z} = \frac{1}{\rho}[\cos (-\theta) + i \sin (-\theta)]$$

$$= \frac{1}{\rho}[\cos \theta - i \sin \theta], \quad \text{since } \sin (-\theta) = -\sin \theta.$$

(i) *Powers and roots.* From the above rule for multiplying complex numbers it follows by a simple induction argument that if $z = \rho(\cos \theta + i \sin \theta)$ and n is any positive integer, then

$$z^n = \rho^n(\cos n\theta + i \sin n\theta).$$

The same relation holds for negative integers n as is seen by using the rule for division. In particular for $\rho = 1$ we have *De Moivre's Theorem*:

$$(\cos \theta + i \sin \theta)^n = \cos n\theta + i \sin n\theta.$$

Now let n be any positive integer. We proceed to find the nth roots of a complex number $\alpha \neq 0$. We set $z^n = \alpha$ and seek solutions for z.

Let $z = \rho(\cos\theta + i\sin\theta)$. Then $\alpha = z^n = \rho^n(\cos n\theta + i\sin n\theta)$. Thus if $\alpha = r[\cos\phi + i\sin\phi]$ we have

$$r = \rho^n, \qquad \phi = n\theta + 2k\pi \qquad (k = 0, 1, 2, \cdots);$$

whence

$$\rho = \sqrt[n]{r} \qquad \theta = \frac{\phi + 2k\pi}{n} \qquad (k = 0, 1, \cdots, n - 1)$$

and clearly the values $k = 0, 1, 2, \cdots, n - 1$ and only these give distinct values of z. Thus we have found exactly the n nth roots

$$z = \sqrt[n]{r}\left[\cos\left(\frac{\phi}{n} + \frac{2k\pi}{n}\right) + i\sin\left(\frac{\phi}{n} + \frac{2k\pi}{n}\right)\right], \qquad k = 0, 1, \cdots, n - 1$$

for the number $\alpha = r[\cos\phi + i\sin\phi]$.

(j) *Absolute values. Inequalities.*

It was shown in (h) above that for any two complex numbers

$$z_1 = x_1 + iy_1, \qquad z_2 = x_2 + iy_2,$$

$$|z_1 z_2| = |z_1|\,|z_2|$$

$$\left|\frac{z_1}{z_2}\right| = \frac{|z_1|}{|z_2|} \qquad z_2 \neq 0.$$

These relations are readily deduced algebraically directly from the definitions of product and quotient. We proceed to show further, the relations

(*)
$$|z_1| - |z_2| \leqq |z_1 + z_2| \leqq |z_1| + |z_2|$$

This follows readily from the Cauchy-Schwarz inequality, I, (14.1). However, we give an elementary proof.

Since for a and b real, $(a - b)^2 \geqq 0$ so that $a^2 + b^2 \geqq 2ab$, we have

$$x_1^2 y_2^2 + x_2^2 y_1^2 \geqq 2x_1 x_2 y_1 y_2.$$

Whence

$$x_1^2 x_2^2 + y_1^2 y_1^2 + 2x_1 x_2 y_1 y_2 \leqq x_1^2 x_2^2 + y_1^2 y_2^2 + x_1^2 y_2^2 + x_2^2 y_1^2$$

or

(i)
$$(x_1 x_2 + y_1 y_2)^2 \leqq (x_1^2 + y_1^2)(x_2^2 + y_2^2).$$

Thus

$$x_1 x_2 + y_1 y_2 \leqq \sqrt{(x_1^2 + y_1^2)(x_2^2 + y_2^2)}$$

or

(ii)
$$2x_1 x_2 + 2y_1 y_2 \leqq 2\sqrt{(x_1^2 + y_1^2)(x_2^2 + y_2^2)},$$

so that

(iii) $(x_1^2 + x_2^2 + 2x_1x_2) + (y_1^2 + y_2^2 + 2y_1y_2)$

$$\leqq x_1^2 + y_1^2 + 2\sqrt{(x_1^2 + y_1^2)(x_2^2 + y_2^2)} + x_2^2 + y_2^2$$

or

(iv) $(x_1 + x_2)^2 + (y_1 + y_2)^2 \leqq (\sqrt{x_1^2 + y_1^2} + \sqrt{x_2^2 + y_2^2})^2 \,.$

Accordingly

(v) $\sqrt{(x_1 + x_2)^2 + (y_1 + y_2)^2} \leqq \sqrt{x_1^2 + y_1^2} + \sqrt{x_2^2 + y_2^2}$

or

$$|z_1 + z_2| \leqq |z_1| + |z_2| \,.$$

Now since it results also from (i) that

$$x_1x_2 + y_1y_2 \geqq - \sqrt{(x_1^2 + y_1^2)(x_2^2 + y_2^2)} \,,$$

we get (ii) and (iii) with the inequality and the sign of the radical reversed and (iv) with the inequality reversed and a minus sign between the radicals. This gives (v) similarly altered or

$$|z_1 + z_2| \geqq |z_1| - |z_2| \,.$$

Of course this is also deducible directly from the other relation in (*) since this latter gives

$$|z_1 + z_2| + |-z_2| \geqq |z_1 + z_2 - z_2| = |z_1|$$

or

$$|z_1 + z_2| \geqq |z_1| - |-z_2| = |z_1| - |z_2| \,.$$

Now for any single complex number $z = x + yi$, since

$$\sqrt{x^2 + y^2} \geqq \sqrt{x^2} = |x|,$$

we have

$$|z| \geqq |x|, \qquad |z| \geqq |y| \text{ so that}$$
$$|z| \geqq \tfrac{1}{2}(|x| + |y|) \,.$$

Also by (*) above

$$|z| = |x + iy| \leqq |x| + |iy| = |x| + |y| \,.$$

Combining we get

(†) $\tfrac{1}{2}(|x| + |y|) \leqq |z| \leqq |x| + |y|$

The fraction $\tfrac{1}{2}$ in (†) can be replaced by $\tfrac{1}{2}\sqrt{2}$. The reader may find it interesting to prove this algebraically.

(k) *The metric.* It results at once from what has been shown above that if we define a metric in the set of complex numbers as $\rho(z_1, z_2) = |z_1 - z_2|$, we have a metric space. For this number vanishes if and only if $z_1 = z_2$ and is symmetric; and for three complex numbers z_1, z_2, z_3, we have

$$|z_1 - z_2| + |z_2 - z_3| \geqq |z_1 - z_3|$$

by (*) above so that the triangle inequality holds. Further, this metric is identical with the ordinary cartesian distance between the points z_1 and z_2 in the complex plane for every pair of complex numbers z_1 and z_2.

(1) *The complex number systems as a topological space.* The topology of the complex number system as given by the metric just defined is identical with that of a euclidean plane because the correspondence between the complex numbers and the points in the complex plane is 1-1 and continuous both ways. The latter results from the fact that the metric $|z_1 - z_2|$ in the complex number system is equal to the distance between the corresponding points in the complex plane for each pair of complex numbers z_1, z_2.

Thus, in particular, the complex number space is separable, metric, connected, locally connected, and locally compact. Every bounded closed set is compact and the space is complete. The *completeness* of the complex number system is readily deduced directly from the fact that *a sequence $z_1, z_2, z_3, \cdots$ of complex numbers converges to a limit $z = x + yi$, $\lim z_n = z$, if and only if both $x_n \to x$ and $y_n \to y$ where $z_n = x_n + iy_n$.* For by relation (†) in (j)

$$\tfrac{1}{2}(|x_n - x| + |y_n - y|) \leqq |z_n - z| \leqq |x_n - x| + |y_n - y|$$

so that $z_n - z \to 0$ if and only if both $x_n - x \to 0$ and $y_n - y \to 0$.

It follows similarly that a sequence $z_1, z_2, \cdots$ of complex numbers is a Cauchy sequence if and only if both (x_n) and (y_n) are Cauchy sequences where $z_n = x_n + iy_n$. Thus if $z_1, z_2, \cdots$ is a Cauchy sequence, since the real number system is complete there exist real numbers x and y such that $x_n \to x$ and $y_n \to y$ and this gives $z_n \to z = x + yi$.

2. Functions of a complex variable. Limits. Continuity.

Any rule or law f which assigns to each complex number z in a set Z of complex numbers one or more definite complex numbers $f(z)$ as values is called a *function of the complex variable z.* Thus a function $f(z)$ is a transformation of the set Z on which it is defined into the complex number system. The function is single valued if it assigns just one value $f(z)$ to each z in the set Z. Unless otherwise specified all our functions are supposed to be single valued. When we deal with multiple valued functions such as $\sqrt{z}$ or arg z we will nearly always limit our considerations to a single branch of these functions on which they are single valued. It will be convenient to write $w = f(z)$ for a function and to consider that the values w of f lie in a separate complex number system. Thus we may think of the values assumed by z as lying in one complex plane, the z-plane, and the values of w as being in another, the w-plane. Of course, these planes are alike in every essential respect and may actually be the same.

Now for any $z = x + iy$ where f is defined let us write $w = f(z) = u + iv$. Then clearly u and v are real valued functions of the real variables x and y. Thus we have

$$w = f(z) = u(x, y) + iv(x, y) .$$

Suppose now that $f(z)$ is defined for all z in a neighborhood of z_0 though not necessarily defined at z_0. Then we define $\lim_{z \to z_0} f(z) = w_0$ in the usual way to mean that for any $\epsilon > 0$ a $\delta > 0$ exists such that

$$\left| f(z) - w_0 \right| < \epsilon \quad \text{provided} \quad \left| z - z_0 \right| < \delta \text{ and } z \neq z_0.$$

It follows at once that $\lim_{z \to z_0} f(z) = w_0 = u_0 + iv_0$ if and only if we have both the simultaneous limits

$$\lim_{\substack{x \to x_0 \\ y \to y_0}} u(x, y) = u_0 \quad \text{and} \quad \lim_{\substack{x \to x_0 \\ y \to y_0}} v(x, y) = v_0.$$

For by the inequality (†) in §1, (i), $\left| f(z) - w_0 \right|$ will be $< \epsilon$ provided $\left| u(x, y) - u_0 \right|$ and $\left| v(x, y) - v_0 \right|$ are each $< \epsilon/2$ and conversely each of these will be $< \epsilon$ provided $\left| f(z) - w_0 \right| < \epsilon/2$.

If $f(z)$ is defined at z_0, $f(z)$ is said to be continuous at z_0 provided $\lim_{z \to z_0} f(z) = f(z_0)$. Clearly this is equivalent to the statement that f is continuous at z_0 when considered as a transformation of its range of definition into the w-plane. Also by what was just shown it results that $f(z)$ is continuous at z_0 if and only if each of the real functions $u(x, y)$ and $v(x, y)$ is continuous in (x, y) simultaneously at the point (x_0, y_0).

The usual theorems on limits and continuity now follow without further proof from the corresponding results for real functions, because we can reduce all such questions to the same questions concerning the pair of real functions $u(x, y)$ and $v(x, y)$. Thus, for example, $\lim_{z \to z_0} f(z) = F$ and $\lim_{z \to z_0} g(z) = G$ give

$$\lim_{z \to z_0} [f(z) \pm g(z)] = F \pm G, \qquad \lim_{z \to z_0} f(z)g(z) = FG$$

and, for $G \neq 0$,

$$\lim_{z \to z_0} \frac{f(z)}{g(z)} = \frac{F}{G} .$$

Likewise any function continuous on a closed and bounded (compact) set K is bounded and uniformly continuous on K; and if $f(z)$ is continuous at z_0 and $g(w)$ is continuous at $w_0 = f(z_0)$, then $gf(z)$ is continuous at z_0. These results also follow from the corresponding results for continuous transformations.

3. Derivatives. Let $w = f(z)$ be defined throughout a neighborhood of z_0 and let Δz be a complex variable. If

$$\lim_{\Delta z \to 0} \frac{f(z_0 + \Delta z) - f(z_0)}{\Delta z}$$

exists and has a definite finite value of $f'(z_0)$, f is said to be differentiable at z_0 and to have $f'(z_0)$ as its derivative at $z = z_0$. For example $w = z^2$ is differentiable and has derivative $2z_0$ for any z_0 whatever, since

$$\lim_{\Delta z \to 0} \frac{(z_0 + \Delta z)^2 - z_0^2}{\Delta z} = \lim_{\Delta z \to 0} (2z_0 + \Delta z) = 2z_0.$$

On the other hand the function $w = \bar{z}$ is nowhere differentiable. For we have (for any z_0)

$$\frac{\Delta w}{\Delta z} = \frac{\Delta x - i\,\Delta y}{\Delta x + i\,\Delta y} \,;$$

and by taking Δz real ($\Delta y = 0$) this ratio can be made to approach 1 whereas by choosing Δz pure imaginary ($\Delta x = 0$) it will approach -1 as $\Delta z \to 0$. Thus the limit fails to exist.

Using the limit theorems referred to in §2 it now follows as in the case of real functions that the sum, difference product and quotient of two differentiable functions are differentiable and that the same relations exist as in the real case. That is, if $f(z)$ and $g(z)$ are differentiable,

$$\frac{d(f \pm g)}{dz} = \frac{df}{dz} \pm \frac{dg}{dz}$$

$$\frac{d(fg)}{dz} = f\frac{dg}{dz} + g\frac{df}{dz}$$

$$\frac{d\,f/g}{dz} = \frac{g\dfrac{df}{dz} - f\dfrac{dg}{dz}}{g^2}, \qquad \text{(where } g(z) \neq 0\text{).}$$

Thus, in particular, all polynomials in z are everywhere differentiable, since obviously $w = z$ is everywhere differentiable.

Also if z and s are complex variables and if $w = f(s)$ is differentiable at $s = s_0$ and $s = g(z)$ is differentiable at $z = z_0$ then the composite function

$$w = fg(z)$$

is differentiable at z_0 and we have

$$\frac{dw}{dz} = \frac{dw}{ds}\frac{ds}{dz}$$

For let

$$\Delta w = \frac{dw}{ds}\Delta s + \epsilon(\Delta s)\Delta s,$$

where

$$\epsilon(\Delta s) = \frac{\Delta w}{\Delta s} - \frac{dw}{ds} \quad \text{for } \Delta s \neq 0$$

$$\epsilon(0) = 0.$$

Then

$$\frac{\Delta w}{\Delta z} = \frac{dw}{ds}\frac{\Delta s}{\Delta z} + \epsilon(\Delta s)\frac{\Delta s}{\Delta z} \quad \text{for all } \Delta s.$$

Whence

$$\frac{dw}{dz} = \lim_{\Delta z \to 0} \frac{\Delta w}{\Delta z} = \frac{dw}{ds}\frac{ds}{dz}.$$

4. Differentiability conditions. Cauchy-Riemann equations. Suppose the function $w = f(z) = u(x, y) + iv(x, y)$ has a derivative at the point z. Then since $\Delta w/\Delta z$ has a limit as $\Delta z \to 0$ and this limit is independent of the way in which $\Delta z \to 0$, let us first take Δz to be real. Then $\Delta z = \Delta x$ and

(a) $f'(z) = \lim\limits_{\Delta z \to 0} \dfrac{\Delta w}{\Delta z} = \lim\limits_{\Delta x \to 0} \dfrac{u(x + \Delta x, y) - u(x, y)}{\Delta x}$

$$+ i \lim_{\Delta x \to 0} \frac{v(x + \Delta x, y) - v(x, y)}{\Delta x}$$

$$= \frac{\partial u}{\partial x} + i\frac{\partial v}{\partial x}.$$

Similarly if we now let Δz be pure imaginary, so that $\Delta z = i\,\Delta y$, we have

(b) $f'(z) = \lim\limits_{\Delta y \to 0} \dfrac{u(x, y + \Delta y) - u(x, y)}{i\Delta y} + \lim\limits_{\Delta y \to 0} \dfrac{v(x, y + \Delta y) - v(x, y)}{\Delta y}$

$$= \frac{\partial v}{\partial y} + \frac{1}{i}\frac{\partial u}{\partial y} = \frac{\partial v}{\partial y} - i\frac{\partial u}{\partial y}$$

Since the two forms (a) and (b) for $f'(z)$ must be identical we have

$$\frac{\partial u}{\partial x} = \frac{\partial v}{\partial y} \quad \text{and} \quad -\frac{\partial u}{\partial y} = \frac{\partial v}{\partial x}$$

These equations which necessarily hold when $f(z)$ has a derivative are known as the Cauchy-Riemann equations.

We now show, conversely, assuming that the functions $u(x, y)$ and $v(x, y)$ have continuous first partial derivatives throughout a neighborhood of a point $z = x + iy$, the holding of the Cauchy-Riemann equations is also sufficient to insure differentiability of the function $w = u + iv$ at that point.

In view of the continuity assumption, the Mean Value Theorem for real functions enables us to write, for any Δz of sufficiently small modulus,

$$\Delta u = \frac{\partial u}{\partial x}\Delta x + \frac{\partial u}{\partial y}\Delta y + \epsilon(\Delta x, \Delta y)\Delta x + \eta(\Delta x, \Delta y)\Delta y$$

$$\Delta v = \frac{\partial v}{\partial x}\Delta x + \frac{\partial v}{\partial y}\Delta y + \gamma(\Delta x, \Delta y)\,\Delta x + \delta(\Delta x, \Delta y)\Delta y$$

where the indicated partial derivatives are evaluated at the point (x, y) and where each of the functions ϵ, η, γ, δ has the limit 0 as $(\Delta x, \Delta y) \to (0, 0)$. Now replacing $\partial u/\partial y$ by $-\partial v/\partial x$ and $\partial v/\partial y$ by $\partial u/\partial x$ (by the Cauchy-Riemann equations) and combining we get

$$\Delta w = \Delta u + i\Delta v = \frac{\partial u}{\partial x}(\Delta x + i\Delta y) + i\frac{\partial v}{\partial x}(\Delta x + i\Delta y)$$
$$+ (\epsilon + i\gamma)\,\Delta x + (\eta + i\delta)\Delta y\,,$$

so that

$$\frac{\Delta w}{\Delta z} = \frac{\partial u}{\partial x} + i\frac{\partial v}{\partial x} + (\epsilon + i\gamma)\frac{\Delta x}{\Delta z} + (\eta + i\delta)\frac{\Delta y}{\Delta z}\,.$$

Since $|\Delta x/\Delta z|$ and $|\Delta y/\Delta z|$ are each ≤ 1 by §1, (j), each of the last two terms has the limit 0 as $\Delta z \to 0$ and thus $\Delta w/\Delta z$ has the limit $\partial u/\partial x + i(\partial v/\partial x)$ as $\Delta z \to 0$ so that $f'(z)$ exists.

5. The exponential and related functions.

For any $z = x + iy$ we define the exponential function

$$e^z = e^x(\cos y + i\sin y)\,.$$

Note that if $z = x$ is real, e^z reduces to the ordinary real value e^x; and if $z = iy$ is pure imaginary we have

$$e^{iy} = \cos y + i\sin y\,.$$

Thus $e^z = e^x e^{iy} = e^{x+iy}$ for any z. For any z,

$$|e^z| = e^x, \quad \arg e^z = y.$$

If we write z in polar form

$$z = \rho(\cos\theta + i\sin\theta),$$

then since $e^{i\theta} = \cos\theta + i\sin\theta$, this also takes the form $z = \rho e^{i\theta}$ which is frequently a most convenient representation of a complex number.

It is now easy to show that the complex exponential function e^z has properties analogous to the real exponential. For example

$$e^{z_1} e^{z_2} = e^{z_1 + z_2}$$

$$\frac{e^{z_1}}{e^{z_2}} = e^{z_1 - z_2}$$

follow from the above together with the multiplication and division rules developed in §1, (h). For

$$e^{z_1} e^{z_2} = e^{x_1} e^{iy_1} e^{x_2} e^{iy_2} = e^{x_1} e^{x_2} e^{iy_1} e^{iy_2} = e^{(x_1+x_2)} e^{i(y_1+y_2)} = e^{z_1+z_2},$$

and similarly for the second relation.

Also, however, we note that for any z,

$$e^{z+2\pi i} = e^{x+i(y+2\pi)} = e^x[\cos(y+2\pi) + i\sin(y+2\pi)] = e^z.$$

Hence the function e^z is periodic of period $2\pi i$.

The exponential function e^z is everywhere differentiable. For if $f(z) = e^z = u + iv = e^x \cos y + ie^x \sin y$, we have

$$\frac{\partial u}{\partial x} = e^x \cos y = \frac{\partial v}{\partial y}, \qquad \frac{\partial u}{\partial y} = -e^x \sin y = -\frac{\partial v}{\partial x},$$

so that the Cauchy-Riemann equations hold and all first partial derivatives are continuous. Further

$$f'(z) = \frac{\partial u}{\partial x} + i\frac{\partial v}{\partial x} = e^x \cos y + ie^x \sin y$$

so that $de^z/dz = e^z$.

Using the exponential function, the trigonometric functions are readily defined

$$\sin z = \frac{e^{iz} - e^{-iz}}{2i}, \qquad \cos z = \frac{e^{iz} + e^{-iz}}{2},$$

$\tan z = \sin z/\cos z$, and so on. The usual properties of these functions are now easily developed. The reader should show, for example, such relations as

$$\sin^2 z + \cos^2 z = 1$$

$$\frac{d}{dz}(\sin z) = \cos z .$$

For any complex number $z \neq 0$ we define

$$\log z = \log \rho + i\theta$$

where $z = \rho e^{i\theta}$ and where $\log \rho$ represents the ordinary real logarithm of the positive number ρ. The logarithm function thus is infinitely many valued, since different values of $\theta = \arg z$ give different values of $\log z$. For any $z \neq 0$ the values of $\log z$ are distributed vertically as points in the complex plane and are 2π units apart. For any one value w_0 of $\log z$ the whole set of values of $\log z$ could be represented in the form $w_0 + 2k\pi i$, $k = 0, \pm 1, \pm 2, \cdots$.

We have at once, for $w = \log z$,

$$e^w = e^{\log \rho + i\theta} = e^{\log \rho} e^{i\theta} = \rho e^{i\theta} = z .$$

Thus $\log z$ is the inverse function to the exponential function.

If for any fixed value θ_0 of θ we restrict θ to values $\theta_0 \leq \theta \leq \theta_0 + 2\pi$, we get only one value of $\log z$ for any $z \neq 0$ and thus we get a single valued *branch* of $\log z$. It is readily verified that any branch of $\log z$ satisfies the Cauchy-Riemann equations at any $z \neq 0$ and thus is differentiable on its whole range of definition. Also,

$$\frac{d \log z}{dz} = \frac{1}{z}$$

as is readily shown by writing

$$\log z = \log \sqrt{x^2 + y^2} + i \arctan \frac{y}{x} \qquad x \neq 0$$

or

$$\log z = \log \sqrt{x^2 + y^2} + i \operatorname{arccot} \frac{x}{y} \qquad \text{for} \qquad y \neq 0$$

and computing

$$f'(z) = \frac{\partial u}{\partial x} + i\frac{\partial v}{\partial x} = \frac{x}{x^2 + y^2} - \frac{iy}{x^2 + y^2} = \frac{1}{z} .$$

V. Topological Index

1. Exponential representations. Indices.

Let $\phi(x)$ be any mapping of a metric space X into the complex plane Z. Let $\phi(X) = E$ and let $p \, \varepsilon \, Z - E$. If there exists a continuous complex valued function $u(x)$ on X such that

(†) $$e^{u(x)} = \phi(x) - p \, , \qquad x \, \varepsilon \, X \, ,$$

we will call (†) an *admissible* exponential representation of $\phi(x) - p$ on X, and $u(x)$ will be called a *continuous branch of the logarithm* of $\phi(x) - p$ on X.

(1.1) *If there exists a ray pq with origin p and lying in $Z - E$, then $\phi(x)$ has an admissible representation* (†) *on X. For any admissible $u(x)$ and any $a, b \, \varepsilon \, X$, the difference in the imaginary parts of $u(a)$ and $u(b)$ is numerically $< 2\pi$. Accordingly $\phi(b) = \phi(a)$ implies $u(b) = u(a)$. Further, $u(a)$ may be any preassigned value whatever of $\log[\phi(a) - p]$.*

For if $u(a) = \log|\phi(a) - p| + i\theta_a$, we have only to define $u(x) = \log|\phi(x) - p| + i(\theta_a + \theta'_x)$ where θ'_x is the signed angle, $-2\pi < \theta'_x < 2\pi$, from the ray $p\phi(a)$ to the ray $p\phi(x)$ not containing the ray pq.

(1.2) *If X is an interval ab, a ray, a line, or a plane, $\phi(x) - p$ always has an admissible exponential representation* (†) *on X. Further, $u(x)$ is uniquely determined up to an additive constant.*

For let $a = x_0, x_1, x_2, \cdots, x_n = b$ be a subdivision of the interval ab so that $\phi(x_i x_{i+1})$ lies inside a circle not enclosing p for each $i = 0, 1, \cdots, n-1$. Then by (1.1), $\phi(x) - p$ has a representation (†) on $x_0 x_1$; and again it has a representation (†) on $x_1 x_2$ where the new $u(x_1)$ agrees with the $u(x_1)$ in the representation on $x_0 x_1$. Likewise there is a representation (†) on $x_2 x$ agreeing at x_2 with the previous one and so on to $x_{n-1} x_n$. Thus we obtain a continuous branch $u(x)$ of $\log(\phi(x) - p)$ on ab. In case X is a ray or a line, clearly a continuation of the same procedure gives a continuous branch $u(x)$ of $\log[\phi(x) - p]$ on X. Now to see that this is unique up to an additive constant, we have only to note that $e^{u(x)} = e^{v(x)}$ on a connected set I implies $u(x) - v(x) = 2k\pi i$ on I for some fixed integer k, because $u(x) - v(x)$ is continuous on I and is always a value of $\log 1$.

Now let X be a plane, which we take as a complex plane with cartesian coordinates (s, t) so that $x = s + it$. As just shown above, $\phi(x) - p$ has an admissible exponential representation on the real axis $t = 0$, giving a continuous branch $u_0(s)$ of log $[\phi(x) - p]$. Further, for each s_0, there is a continuous branch $u_{s_0}(t)$ of log $[\phi(x) - p]$ on the vertical line $s = s_0$ so chosen that $u_{s_0}(0) = u_0(s_0)$. For each point $x \,\varepsilon\, X$ we define

$$u(x) = u(s, t) = u_s(t), \qquad \text{where } x = s + it.$$

Then $e^{u(x)} = \phi(x) - p$ for each $x \,\varepsilon\, X$ and we shall show that $u(x)$ is continuous. To this end we first prove the

LEMMA. If on a rectangle R: $s_0 \leqq s \leqq s'$, $t_0 \leqq t \leqq t'$,

(i) $\qquad \left| \arg [\phi(x_1) - p] - \arg [\phi(x_2) - p] \right| < \pi, \qquad x_1, x_2 \,\varepsilon\, R$

(ii) $\qquad u(x)$ is continuous on the base $t = t_0$, $s_0 \leqq s \leqq s'$ of R,

then $u(x)$ is continuous at all points of R.

Since by (i) there is a ray from p not meeting $\phi(R)$, it follows by (1.1) that there is a continuous branch $v(x)$ of log $[\phi(x) - p]$ on R, and we suppose this chosen so that $v(x_0) = u(x_0)$ where $x_0 = s_0 + it_0$. It then follows that $u(x) \equiv v(x)$ on R so that $u(x)$ is continuous on R. For let $w(x) = v(x) - u(x)$, $x \,\varepsilon\, R$; and define

$$g(r) = w(s_0 + r, t_0),$$

for $0 \leqq r \leqq s - s_0$,

$$g(r) = w(s, t_0 + r - s + s_0),$$

for $s - s_0 \leqq r \leqq t - t_0 + s - s_0 = q$. Then since $u(x)$, and therefore $w(x)$, is continuous on the base of R and is also continuous in t on the vertical line through (s, t_0) and (s, t) where $u(x)$ is identical with $u_s(t)$, it follows that $g(r)$ is continuous in r on the interval $0 \leqq r \leqq q$. Now since $e^{v(x)} = e^{u(x)} = \phi(x) - p$ for all $x \,\varepsilon\, R$ so that $e^{w(x)} = e^{v(x) - u(x)} \equiv 1$ on R, we have $e^{g(r)} \equiv 1$ on $(0, q)$. Thus $g(r)$ is of the form $2k\pi i$ where k is an integer, so that $g(r)$ must be constant on $(0, q)$ as this interval is connected. Thus $g(r) \equiv 0$ on $(0, q)$ since $g(0) = w(s_0, t_0) = v(x_0) - v(x_0) = 0$.

This proves the lemma; and it now follows readily that $u(x)$ is continuous on any rectangle Q with a base on the s-axis and thus is continuous throughout the whole plane. For by uniform continuity of $\phi(x)$ on Q, Q can be divided by horizontal and vertical lines into a finite number of subrectangles such that (i) holds on each of them. Then since each point x_1 in Q can be joined to the base of Q on the s-axis by a chain $Q_1, Q_2, \cdots, Q_n$ of these subrectangles each having a base in common with its predecessor and where Q_1 has a base on the s-axis and $x_1 \,\varepsilon\, Q_n$, repeated application of the lemma to this chain gives continuity of $u(x)$ on Q_n and thus at x_1.

Thus $e^{u(x)} = \phi(x) - p$ is an admissible exponential representation on X; and uniqueness follows as before.

(1.21) COROLLARY. *The same conclusions as on* (1.2) *hold in case* X *is any region of the form* $-\infty < s < \infty$, $a \leq t \leq b$ *or of the form* $c \leq s < \infty$, $a \leq t \leq b$ *in an* (s, t) *plane, or where* X *is any rectangle in a plane. Further, the property thus defined on* X *is a topological invariant, so that the same conclusions hold on any set* X' *homeomorphic with a set* X *on which they hold.*

We now limit our considerations to the case in which X is an interval or a simple arc ab.

DEFINITION. For any admissible exponential representation $e^{u(x)}$ of $\phi(x) - p$ on ab we define

$$\mu_{ab}(\phi, p) = u(b) - u(a) .$$

When no confusion is likely to result, some or all of the symbols ab, ϕ and p in the expression $\mu_{ab}(\phi, p)$ may be omitted. We have immediately the following:

Notes.

(i) *The index* μ *is independent of the particular* $u(x)$ *used in the exponential representation.*

(ii) *For any* $\phi(x)$ *and any* $p \; \varepsilon \; Z - E$

$$\mu(\phi, p) = \mu(\phi - p, 0).$$

(iii) *For any factorization* $\phi(x) - p = \phi_1(x) \cdot \phi_2(x)$, *we have* $\mu(\phi, p) = \mu(\phi_1, 0) + \mu(\phi_2, 0)$.

(iv) *If* $l(z)$ *is any non-singular linear transformation of the* z-*plane into itself*, $\mu[l\phi, l(p)] = \mu(\phi, p)$.

Note (ii) is a trivial consequence of the definition and (i) is a restatement of part of (1.2). To see (iii), we take representations

$$\phi(x) - p = e^{u(x)}, \qquad \phi_1(x) = e^{u_1(x)}, \qquad \phi_2(x) = e^{u_2(x)}.$$

Then

$$e^{u_1(x) + u_2(x)} = \phi_1(x)\phi_2(x) = e^{u(x)}$$

gives

$$\mu(\phi_1, 0) + \mu(\phi_2, 0) = u_1(b) - u_1(a) + u_2(b) - u_2(a)$$
$$= u(b) - u(a) = \mu(\phi, p),$$

by (1.2).

Note (iv) is a direct consequence of (ii) and (iii). For let $l(z) = \alpha z + \beta$ where α and β are constants, $\alpha \neq 0$. Then $l\phi = \alpha\phi + \beta$, $l(p) = \alpha p + \beta$ and (ii) gives

$$\mu[l\phi, l(p)] = \mu(\alpha\phi + \beta, \alpha p + \beta) = \mu(\alpha\phi - \alpha p, 0) = \mu(\alpha\phi, \alpha p);$$

and since obviously the index of any constant function about any point different from that constant value is 0, (iii) gives

$$\mu(\alpha\phi, \alpha p) = \mu[\alpha(\phi - p), 0] = \mu(\alpha, 0) + \mu(\phi, p) = \mu(\phi, p).$$

(1.3) *If $\phi(b) = \phi(a)$, then $(1/2\pi i)\mu(\phi, p)$ is integer valued and continuous in p. Thus it is constant in each component of $Z - E$.*

For if $g(x) = (p_1 - p_2)/[\phi(x) - p]$, $x \, \varepsilon \, ab$, we have

$$\phi(x) - p_1 = (\phi(x) - p)[g(x) - (-1)].$$

Thus by notes (ii) and (iii)

$$\mu(\phi, p_1) = \mu(\phi, p) + \mu(g, -1).$$

Also if p_1 is any point inside the circle with center p and radius $\rho(p, E)$, $g(E)$ lies within the circle $|z| = 1$ and does not intersect the ray of the negative real axis from -1 to ∞, so that $\mu(g, -1) = 0$ by (1.1).

(1.4) *If $\phi(a) = \phi(b)$, then $\mu(\phi, p) = 0$ for all points p in the unbounded component Q of $Z - E$.*

For there exists a point $p_1 \, \varepsilon \, Q$ which is the origin of a ray lying wholly in Q. Thus by (1.1) and (1.3), $\mu(\phi, p_1) = 0 = \mu(\phi, p)$.

(1.5) *For any homeomorphism $h(ab) = \alpha\beta$ which preserves sense [i.e., $h(a) = \alpha$], we have*

$$\mu_{ab}(\phi, p) = \mu_{\alpha\beta}(\phi h^{-1}, p).$$

For if $\phi_1(x) = \phi h^{-1}(x)$ and $u_1(x) = u h^{-1}(x)$, $x \, \varepsilon \, \alpha\beta$, where $e^{u(x)} = \phi(x) - p$, $x \, \varepsilon \, ab$, we have

$$e^{u_1(x)} = e^{u h^{-1}(x)} = \phi h^{-1}(x) - p = \phi_1(x) - p, \qquad x \, \varepsilon \, \alpha\beta,$$

and

$$u_1(\beta) - u_1(\alpha) = u h^{-1}(\beta) - u h^{-1}(\alpha) = u(b) - u(a).$$

(1.6) *Given $\phi(x) = f\zeta(x)$, $x \, \varepsilon \, ab$, where ζ and f are continuous on ab and $\zeta(ab)$ respectively. If $\zeta(a) = \zeta(b)$, then $\zeta(a)$ may be taken as an arbitrarily given point of $H = \zeta(ab)$ without affecting the value of $\mu_{ab}(\phi, p)$.*

For let $q \, \varepsilon \, H - \zeta(a)$ and let $\alpha \, \varepsilon \, \zeta^{-1}(q)$. We suppose, as we may by (1.5), that ab is an interval and let $\beta = b - a + \alpha$. Then if $e^{u(x)} = \phi(x) - p$ is an admissible representation on ab, we define

$$\phi_1(x) = \phi(x), \text{ for } \alpha \leq x \leq b$$
$$\phi_1(x) = \phi(x - b + a), \text{ for } b \leq x \leq \beta$$
$$u_1(x) = u(x), \text{ for } \alpha \leq x \leq b$$
$$u_1(x) = u(x - b + a) + u(b) - u(a) \text{ for } b \leq x \leq \beta.$$

Then $\phi_1(x)$ and $u_1(x)$ are continuous on $\alpha\beta$ and we have

$$e^{u_1(x)} = e^{u(x)} = \phi(x) - p = \phi_1(x) - p \quad \text{for} \quad \alpha \leqq x \leqq b$$

$$e^{u_1(x)} = e^{u(x-b+a)+u(b)-u(a)} = e^{u(b)-u(a)} e^{u(x-b+a)} = \phi(x - b + a) - p$$

$$= \phi_1(x) - p,$$

for $b \leqq x \leqq \beta$, since $e^{u(b)-u(a)} = 1$; and

$$u_1(\beta) - u_1(\alpha) = u(\alpha) + u(b) - u(a) - u(\alpha) = u(b) - u(a).$$

2. Traversals of simple arcs and simple closed curves.

Let t be a simple arc and let $f(x)$ be any continuous function from t to the complex plane. If we understand by a *traversal* of t a homeomorphism h of an interval ab onto t, then since as shown in §1, $\mu_{ab}(fh, p) = \mu_{h(a)h(b)}(f, p)$, it follows that $\mu_{ab}(fh, p)$ can be computed most simply directly from t and that its value depends only on the sense α, β or β, α on t in which it is taken, where α and β denote the end points of t. Thus we have

$$\mu_{ab}(fh, p) = \mu_{\alpha\beta}(f, p) = -\mu_{\beta\alpha}(f, p)$$

when $h(a) = \alpha$. Accordingly, indexes μ for functions taken over simple arcs t will be indicated directly on t with the sense shown by the order of the end points α and β of t. In case f is the identity function on t, f will be omitted and we write simply $\mu_{\alpha\beta}(p)$ or $\mu_{\alpha\beta}$ when p is fixed in a discussion.

We note further that for any subdivision $\alpha = x_0, x_1, x_2, \cdots, x_n = \beta$ of t it is obvious that

$$\mu_{\alpha\beta}(f, p) = \sum_0^{n-1} \mu_{x_i x_{i+1}}(f, p).$$

Let J be a simple closed curve and let f be a continuous function from J to the complex plane. If we understand by a *traversal* of J a mapping ζ of an interval or simple arc ab onto J with $\zeta(a) = \zeta(b)$ but with $\zeta^{-1}(y)$ unique for $y \, \varepsilon \, J - \zeta(a)$, it is readily shown that $\mu_{ab}(f\zeta, p)$ depends only on the *sense* in which ζ traverses J. That is, if α, β and γ are distinct points on J, then μ depends on whether, as x moves from a to b on ab, $\zeta(x)$ takes on in turn an even or an odd permutation of the order α, β, γ of these values. Further, the value of μ is independent of the starting point $\zeta(a)$. Indeed we have

(2.1) *For any two sense agreeing traversals ζ and ζ_1 of a simple closed curve J we have*

$$\mu(f\zeta, p) = \mu(f\zeta_1, p).$$

For let ζ and ζ_1 be sense agreeing traversals of J. Let $\phi = f\zeta$, $\phi_1 = f\zeta_1$. Then supposing, as we may by (1.6), that $\zeta(a) = \zeta_1(a_1)$ (where

ζ_1 maps a_1b_1 onto J), $h(x) = \zeta_1^{-1} \zeta(x)$ for $x \neq a, b$, $h(a) = a_1$, $h(b) = b_1$ is a sense preserving homeomorphism of ab onto a_1b_1. Whence $\phi h^{-1} = f\zeta\zeta^{-1} \zeta_1 = f\zeta_1 = \phi_1$; and by (1.5),

$$\mu_{ab}(\phi, p) = \mu_{a_1b_1}(\phi_1, p),$$

which is our desired conclusion.

Thus for any two traversals ζ and ζ_1 of J we have $\mu(f\zeta, p) = \pm\mu(f\zeta_1, p)$ the sign being $+$ or $-$ according as ζ and ζ_1 agree or disagree in sense. Thus if α, β and γ are any three distinct points of J and $\alpha\beta, \beta\gamma, \gamma\alpha$ denote the arcs of J containing just two of these points, then for any traversal ζ of J we have

(*) $$\mu(f\zeta, p) = \pm[\mu_{\alpha\beta}(f, p) + \mu_{\beta\gamma}(f, p) + \mu_{\gamma\alpha}(f, p)].$$

Accordingly we write $\mu_{\alpha\beta\gamma}(f, p)$ for the index taken over J in the sense giving the $+$ sign in (*), i.e., when an even permutation of the order α, β, γ of these values is taken on in turn as x traverses the parameter range ab, and $\mu_{\alpha\gamma\beta\alpha}(f, p)$ for the opposite sense.

Now if C is a circle with center p and radius r, it follows from (2.1) that any traversal of C agreeing in sense with that defined by

$$\zeta(x) - p = e^{2\pi ix + \log r}, \quad 0 \leq x \leq 1, \quad x \text{ real},$$

has index $\mu(\zeta, p) = 2\pi i$ and all other traversals of C have index $-2\pi i$ as they agree in sense with $\overline{\zeta(x)} - p$. (Here we are taking the function f to be the identity mapping $f(z) = z$ and the bar indicates the complex conjugate.)

A similar conclusion holds in the case of any simple closed curve as we now show

(2.2) *For any traversal ζ of a simple closed curve J in the complex plane and any point p within J we have*

$$\frac{1}{2\pi i} \mu_J(\zeta, p) = \pm 1.$$

Proof. Let apb be the interval of the horizontal line through p which contains p and has only its ends in common with J and where a is the right end of apb. Let C be a circle with center p and lying entirely within J and let u and v be the points of ap and pb which are on C. Let s and t be interior points on the upper and lower semi-circles respectively of C with ends u and v. Let x and y be interior points on the arcs of J from a to b such that p is without the simple closed curves

$$J_1 = au + usv + vb + bxa$$

and

$$J_2 = au + utv + vb + bya$$

Now since by (1.4), for any traversals and for the identity function we have

$$\mu_{J_1}(p) = \mu_{J_2}(p) = 0,$$

we obtain by direct computation of indexes over the arcs concerned

$$\mu_{axb} = \mu_{au} + \mu_{usv} + \mu_{vb}$$

$$\mu_{bya} = \mu_{bv} + \mu_{vtu} + \mu_{ua}.$$

Adding we get, since end terms cancel,

$$\mu_{+J} = \mu_{axbya} = \mu_{axb} + \mu_{bya} = \mu_{usv} + \mu_{vtu} = \mu_{+C} = 2\pi i$$

Similarly, of course, $\mu_{-J} = \mu_{aybxa} = \mu_{-C} = -2\pi i$.

DEFINITION. If J is a simple closed curve in the complex plane, by a *positive traversal* of J is meant a traversal ζ of J for which

$$(1/2\pi i)\mu(\zeta, p) = 1$$

where p is any point within J.

It is now clear from (2.1) and (2.2) that if f is any continuous complex valued function defined on J, then all positive traversals of J give the same value $\mu_J(f, q)$ of $\mu(f, q)$ for any q not in $f(J)$ and similarly all negative traversals give this index the same value $\mu_{-J}(f, q)$ and that

$$\mu_{-J}(f, q) = -\mu_J(f, q).$$

Thus we can compute the index μ directly from J; and if α, β, γ are distinct points of J, we have

$$\pm\mu_J(f, q) = \mu_{\alpha\beta\gamma}(f, q) = \mu_{\alpha\beta}(f, q) + \mu_{\beta\gamma}(f, q) + \mu_{\gamma\alpha}(f, q),$$

the sign being $+$ or $-$ according as the order α, β, γ determines the positive or the negative sense on J.

If J and J' are simple closed curves in a plane and a, b, c and a', b', c' respectively are triples of distinct points on J and J', the senses determined by the orders a, b, c on J and a', b', c' on J' are said to *agree* provided that if p and p' are points interior to J and J' respectively then $\mu_{abc}(p) = \mu_{a'b'c'}(p')$. In other words, the senses a, b, c and a', b', c' agree or disagree according as the signs of $1/2\pi i$ times the corresponding circulation indices agree or disagree.

Now let J' be within J. We then can take $p = p'$ since p' is within both J' and J. In this case we show

(2.3) *The senses a, b, c and a', b', c' and J and J' agree if and only if there exist disjoint simple arcs aa', bb', cc' lying except for their ends in the annular region A between J and J'.*

Proof. Suppose such arcs exist. Then since p is without each of the simple closed curves

$$J_c = ab + bb' + b'a' + a'a$$
$$J_a = bc + cc' + c'b' + b'b$$
$$J_b = ca + aa' + a'c' + c'c,$$

we have $0 = \mu_{J_c}(p) + \mu_{J_a}(p) + \mu_{J_b}(p)$. Thus by direct computation with cancellation,

$$0 = \mu_{ab} + \mu_{bc} + \mu_{ca} + \mu_{b'a'} + \mu_{c'b'} + \mu_{a'c'} = \mu_J(p) - \mu_{J'}(p).$$

This gives our assertion that a, b, c agrees with a', b', c'.

Now suppose the senses a, b, c and a', b', c' on J and J' respectively agree, but that arcs aa', bb', cc' do not exist as asserted. Then there do exist disjoint arcs aa' and bb' lying except for their ends in the annular region between J and J'. Now c can be joined to a point c'' on $J' - a' - b'$ by an arc cc'' lying in A except for its ends and not intersecting aa' or bb'; and since c' cannot be so joined, c'' must be on the arc $a'b'$ of J' and not on $a'c'b'$ of J'. But then by the first part of this proof, the senses a, b, c and a', b', c'' would have to agree. Clearly this is impossible because a', b', c'' and a', b', c' are opposite senses on J' whereas they both agree with a, b, c on J. This contradiction shows that arcs aa', bb', cc' must exist as asserted.

(2.31) COROLLARY. *Let J and J' be simple closed curves bounding an annular region A in a plane and let a, b, c and a', b', c' be triples of distinct points on J and J'. If the senses a, b, c and a', b', c' agree so also will the senses $h(a)$, $h(b)$, $h(c)$ and $h(a')$, $h(b')$, $h(c')$ on $h(J)$ and $h(J')$ agree where h is any homeomorphism of $A + J + J'$ into a plane. Thus "agreement in sense" is a topological invariant in this situation.*

DEFINITION. If two 2-cells A and A' with edges J and J' respectively lie together in the interior of a 2-cell E with boundary C, we may now define traversals ζ and ζ' of J and J' as *agreeing in sense* provided each agrees with one and the same traversal of C. This definition will be complete as soon as we define "agreement in sense" for the case where A' lies entirely interior to A, which we now proceed to do. In any situation in which two simple closed curves J and J' are disjoint and constitute the boundary of a "cylinder" surface D, i.e. a set homeomorphic with a closed circular ring, *senses a, b, c and a', b', c' of J and J' are said to agree* provided there exist disjoint simple arcs aa', bb', cc' lying except for their ends interior to the surface D.

From (2.3) we have at once

(2.32) *If A is a 2-cell, "agreement in sense" for two simple closed curves interior to A is invariant under any homeomorphism on A.*

(2.4) *If $J = xay + xby$ and $J_1 = xay + xcy$ are simple closed curves in the plane or on a 2-cell having an arc xay in common, then*

(i) *If the interior of J contains the interior of J_1, then positive traversals of J and J_1 agree in sense on the common arc xay.*

(ii) *If the interiors of J and J_1 are disjoint, positive traversals of J and J_1 are opposite in sense on the common arc xay.*

Proof. By (2.32) there is no loss in generality in assuming that J and J_1 lie in a plane. Statement (i) is a direct consequence of (2.3) because a circle C may be taken interior to both J and J_1 and disjoint arcs xx', aa', yy' in the annular region between J_1 and C will exist with x', a', y' ε C. Then if $yaxby$ is the positive traversal of J, $yaxcy$ must be the positive traversal of J_1 since y, a, x agrees in sense in both cases with the sense y', a', x' on C.

To prove (ii) let p and p_1 be points interior to J and J_1 respectively. We may suppose the positive traversal of J is in the order $yaxby$. Then $xbycx$ is the positive traversal of the simple closed curve $K = xby + xcy$; and since K also encloses p_1, then $xaycx$ must be the positive traversal of J_1 by (i). As xay and yax are opposite, we have established (ii).

DEFINITION. A homeomorphism $h(x)$ of a plane X into a plane Y is *positive* (negative) provided that if $\zeta(t)$ is a positive traversal of a simple closed curve C in X, then $h\zeta(t)$ is a positive (resp. negative) traversal of $h(C)$ in Y. In other words, $h(x)$ is positive provided

(*) $$\mu_C[h\zeta, h(p)] = \mu_C[\zeta, p] \qquad \text{for any } C, \zeta \text{ and } p.$$

As an immediate consequence of (2.3) we have

(2.5) THEOREM. *Given a homeomorphism $h(x)$ of X into Y (planes). If there exists one simple closed curve C in X and a traversal ζ of C such that (*) holds, then (*) holds for arbitrary C, ζ and p so that h is a positive homeomorphism.*

Also as a consequence of *Note* (iv) of § 1 just following the definition of the index μ, we have

(2.6) *Any non-singular linear transformation of a complex plane into itself is a positive homeomorphism.*

Finally, we record the immediate result.

(2.7) *If $h_1(X) = Y$ and $h_2(Y) = Z$ are positive homeomorphisms, so also is $h(X) = Z$ where $h(x) = h_2 h_1(x)$.*

For since $h_1\zeta$ is a positive traversal of $h_1(C)$ in Y, $h_2 h_1 \zeta$ $(=h\zeta)$ is a positive traversal of $h_2 h_1(C)$ $[=h(C)]$ in Z because h_2 is positive.

3. Index invariance.

(3.1) THEOREM. *If $\phi(x)$ and $\phi_1(x)$ are mappings of an arc or interval* *ab into Z satisfying* $\left|\phi_1(x) - \phi(x)\right| < \left|\phi(x) - p\right|$ *on ab and if* $\phi(a) = \phi_1(a)$ *and* $\phi(b) = \phi_1(b)$, *then*

$$\mu_{ab}(\phi, p) = \mu_{ab}(\phi_1, p).$$

Proof. If we take a representation

$$e^{u(x)} = \phi(x) - p, \qquad x \; \varepsilon \; ab,$$

then

$$u(x) = log \left|\phi(x) - p\right| + i\theta(x).$$

Since for each x the circle with center $\phi(x) - p$ and radius $\left|\phi_1(x) - \phi(x)\right|$ neither contains nor encloses the origin, there is a unique $\theta_1(x)$ satisfying

(i) $e^{log \left|\phi_1(x) - p\right| + i\theta_1(x)} = \phi_1(x) - p$

and

(ii) $\theta(x) - \pi/2 < \theta_1(x) < \theta(x) + \pi/2$

If we set $u_1(x) = log \left|\phi_1(x) - p\right| + i\theta_1(x)$, $x \; \varepsilon \; ab$, then $u_1(x)$ is continuous and we have

(iii) $u(b) - u_1(b) = i[\theta(b) - \theta_1(b)],$ since $\phi(b) = \phi_1(b)$

(iv) $u(a) - u_1(a) = i[\theta(a) - \theta_1(a)],$ since $\phi(a) = \phi_1(a).$

Subtracting (iv) from (iii) we get

(v) $\mu_{ab}(\phi, p) - \mu_{ab}(\phi_1, p) = i\{[\theta(b) - \theta_1(b)] - [\theta(a) - \theta_1(a)]\}$
$$= 2\pi i(k_b - k_a),$$

where k_b and k_a are integers. But also by (ii) $\left|\theta(b) - \theta_1(b)\right|$ and $\left|\theta(a) - \theta_1(a)\right|$ are each $< \pi/2$ so that the left member of (v) is numerically $< \pi$ and hence vanishes, because $k_b = k_a$.

(3.11) COROLLARY. *If* $\phi(x)$ *and* $\phi_1(x)$ *are mappings of ab into Z satisfying* $\left|\phi_1(x) - \phi(x)\right| < \left|\phi(x) - p\right|$ *on ab and if* $\phi(a) = \phi(b)$ *and* $\phi_1(a) = \phi_1(b)$, *then*

$$\mu_{ab}(\phi, p) = \mu_{ab}(\phi_1, p).$$

(3.12) COROLLARY. *If* $f(z)$ *and* $f_1(z)$ *are mappings of a simple closed curve C into Z and if* $\left|f_1(z) - f(z)\right| < \left|f(z) - p\right|$ *on C, then*

$$\mu_C(f, p) = \mu_C(f_1, p) \, .$$

For if ζ is a traversal of C and $\phi = f\zeta$, $\phi_1 = f_1\zeta$, (3.11) gives $\mu_{ab}(f\zeta, p) = \mu_{ab}(f_1\zeta, p)$ which is identical with our desired conclusion by (3.1).

(3.13) COROLLARY. *As a function of* f, $\mu_C(f, p)$ *is constant on each component of the mapping space* $(Z - p)^C$, *i.e., the space of all mappings of a simple closed curve C into* $Z - p$.

(3.14) *Similarly, as a function of* f, $\mu_{ab}(f, p)$ *is constant on each component of the space of all mappings of the simple arc* ab *into* $Z - p$ *which agree on the end points of* ab.

(3.2) *Let* $f(x)$ *be a mapping of a separable metric space* X *into* Z *and let* ab *and* $a_1 b_1$ *be simple arcs in* X. *If there exists a homeomorphism* $h(ab) = a_1 b_1$ *with* $h(a) = a_1$ *and satisfying*

$$\left| f(x) - fh(x) \right| < \left| f(x) - p \right|, \qquad x \; \varepsilon \; ab,$$

and

$$f(a) = fh(a) = f(a_1) = \alpha, \qquad f(b) = fh(b) = f(b_1) = \beta,$$

then

$$\mu_{ab}(f, p) = \mu_{a_1 b_1}(f, p).$$

Proof. By (3.1) we have

$$\mu_{ab}(f, p) = \mu_{ab}(fh, p);$$

and since h is a sense preserving homeomorphism of ab onto $a_1 b_1$ $\mu_{ab}(fh, p) = \mu_{a_1 b_1}(f, p)$ by (1.5).

By iteration of (3.2) we get

(3.21) COROLLARY. *Given a mapping* $f(x)$ *of* X *into* Z *as in* (3.2) *and two points* α, β *in* $Z - p$. *For any sequence of simple arcs* $a_1 b_1, a_2 b_2, \cdots$ *joining* $f^{-1}(\alpha)$ *and* $f^{-1}(\beta)$ [*i.e.* $a_i \; \varepsilon \; f^{-1}(\alpha)$, $b_i \; \varepsilon \; f^{-1}(\beta)$] *for which sense preserving homeomorphisms* $h_i(a_i b_i) = a_{i+1} b_{i+1}$, $i = 1, 2, \cdots$ *exist satisfying*

$$\left| f(x) - fh_i(x) \right| < \left| f(x) - p \right|, \qquad x \; \varepsilon \; a_i b_i,$$

we have

$$\mu_{a_1 b_1}(f, p) = \mu_{a_n b_n}(f, p).$$

(3.3) *Given a mapping* $f(x)$ *of a separable metric space* X *into* $Z - p$ *and two points* $\alpha, \beta \; \varepsilon \; Z - p$. *If* H *is any continuous family of simple arcs*

$$H = [h(s, t)], \qquad 0 \leq s \leq 1, 0 \leq t \leq 1,$$

where $h(0, t) = \alpha$, $h(1, t) = \beta$ *for all* t *and* $h(s, t)$ *continuous in* (s, t), *for any two arcs* t_1 *and* t_2 *whatever in* H *we have*

$$\mu_{t_1}(f, p) = \mu_{t_2}(f, p).$$

Similarly for simple closed curves in X, corresponding to (3.2) we have

(3.4) *Let* $f(x)$ *be a mapping of a separable metric space* X *into* Z *and let* C *and* C_1 *be simple closed curves in* X. *If there exists a sense preserving homeomorphism* $h(C) = C_1$ *satisfying*

$$\left| f(x) - fh(x) \right| < \left| f(x) - p \right|, \qquad x \; \varepsilon \; C,$$

then

$$\mu_C(f, p) = \mu_{C_1}(f, p).$$

Corresponding to (3.4) we have

(3.5) *For any mapping f of X into $Z - p$, $\mu_C(f, p)$ is constant on any continuous family $H = [h(s, t)]$ of simple closed curves in X.*

4. Traversals of region boundaries and region subdivisions.

Let R be an elementary region, i.e., a bounded plane region whose boundary consists of a finite number of disjoint simple closed curve $J_0, J_1, \cdots, J_n$, where J_0 encloses $J_1 + J_2 + \cdots + J_n$ and is thus the outer boundary of R. By a positive traversal of $Fr(R)$ is meant a collection of traversals of $J_0, \cdots, J_n$ which is positive on J_0 and negative on $J_1, \cdots, J_n$. It is clear from the above that if f is any continuous function defined on $Fr(R)$, and $\zeta = (\zeta_0, \cdots, \zeta_n)$ and $\zeta' = (\zeta_0', \cdots, \zeta_u')$ are arbitrary positive traversals of $Fr(R)$ then

$$\mu(f\zeta, p) = \sum \mu_{a_i b_i}(f\zeta_i, p) = \sum \mu_{a_i' b_i'}(f\zeta_i', p) = \mu(f\zeta', p),$$

i.o.w., $\mu(f\zeta, p)$ is independent of the particular positive traversals.

Now let f be a continuous function defined on a graph G which includes $Fr(R)$ and lies in $\bar{R}$ and subdivides R into a finite number of regions $R_1, \cdots, R_m$ each bounded by a simple closed curve C_i of G and where the intersection of any two of the C_i is either a vertex or an edge of G. A set A is a graph provided it is the sum of a finite set V of points, called *vertices*, and a finite number of open arcs $\alpha_1, \alpha_2, \cdots, \alpha_n$, called *edges*, so that the two end points of each edge α are distinct and belong to V.

Next let $\zeta = (\zeta_1, \cdots, \zeta_m)$ be a traversal of G obtained by taking positive traversals ζ_i of the C_i. This is called a positive traversal of such a G. Then each edge of G which lies interior to R lies on exactly two of the C_i and by (2.3), (ii), above is traversed in opposite senses by ζ. Further, any edge of G lying on J_0 lies on just one C_i and is traversed positively by ζ by (2.3), (i), since R_i lies interior to R; and similarly an edge of G lying on a J_i with $i \geq 1$ is traversed negatively just once by ζ, since the R_j is exterior to J_i, where R_j is the interior of the C_j containing the edge. Hence we have the

(4.1) LEMMA. *For any positive traversal ζ of a subdivision G of the elementary region R and any continuous complex valued function defined on G we have*

$$\mu_{Fr(R)}(f\zeta, p) = \sum_0^n \mu_{J_i}(f\zeta, p) = \sum_1^m \mu_{C_i}(f\zeta, p) = \mu_G(f\zeta, p)$$

where $p \, \varepsilon \, Z - f(G)$ and where, in general, $\mu_X(\phi, p)$ refers to the index computed over those intervals mapping into X under the traversal ζ. Further $\mu_{Fr(R)}(f\zeta, p)$ is independent of the particular traversal ζ.

In view of the last statement together with the fact that $\mu_{Fr(R)}$ is also independent of the particular subdivision G, the ζ will usually be omitted and we shall write $\mu_{Fr(R)}(f, p)$.

(4.2) THEOREM. *Let R be an elementary region with boundary $C = \sum_0^n J_i$ and let f be any mapping of $\bar{R}$ onto a set E in the complex plane Z. Then for any point p in $Z - E$,*

$$\mu_C(f, p) = 0.$$

Proof. Let G be an admissible subdivision of R with mesh small enough that for each region R_i into which R is divided by G we have

$$\delta[f(R_i)] < \rho(p, E).$$

Then since p is in the unbounded component of $Z - f(\bar{R}_i)$, we have $\mu_{Fr(R_i)}(f\zeta, p) = 0$ for each i, where ζ is any positive traversal of G; and thus $\mu_C(f, p) = \sum \mu_{Fr(R_i)}(f\zeta, p) = 0$ by the lemma (4.1).

(4.21) COROLLARY. *If ζ is a traversal of $Fr(R)$ which is positive on each of the curves J_i, $0 \leq i \leq n$,*

$$\mu_{J_0}(f\zeta, p) = \sum_1^n \mu_{J_i}(f\zeta, p).$$

(4.22) COROLLARY. *If R is an elementary region with boundary C and f is any mapping of C into $Z - p$ which admits an extension over R into $Z - p$, then $\mu_C(f, p) = 0$.*

5. Homotopy. Index invariance.

Two mappings $f(x)$ and $g(x)$ of one metric space X into another one Y are said to be *homotopic* (on X relative to Y) provided there exists a function $f(x, t)$ defined for each $x \,\varepsilon\, X$ and $t \,\varepsilon\, (0, 1)$ and with values in Y which is continuous in (x, t) everywhere and satisfies

$$h(x, 0) \equiv f(x), \qquad h(x, 1) \equiv g(x) \qquad \text{for all } x \,\varepsilon\, X.$$

In other words, f and g are *homotopic* if they can be joined by a continuous family of mappings of X into Y or provided there is a continuous function h of the cartesian product space $X \times I$ into Y, where $I = (0, 1)$, which agrees with $f(x)$ on $X \times (0)$ and with $g(x)$ on $X \times (1)$. We shall write $f \simeq g$ to mean "f and g are homotopic".

Now in case the space X is compact so also is $X \times I$; and if $f \simeq g$, uniform continuity of $h(x, t)$ yields that for any $t_0 \,\varepsilon\, I$ and $\epsilon > 0$ a $\delta > 0$ exists such that

$$\rho[h(x, t), h(x, t_0)] < \epsilon$$

for all $x \varepsilon X$ provided $|t - t_0| < \delta$. Accordingly, by (3.12) and (3.13) we have

(5.1) THEOREM. *If $f(x)$ and $g(x)$ are mappings of a simple closed curve C into $Z - p$ and f and g are homotopic (on C rel. to $Z - p$), then*

$$\mu_C(f, p) = \mu_C(g, p).$$

Our next objective will be to show the invariance of the index μ when the image plane is subjected to an arbitrary positive homeomorphism. Some further developments on homotopy are needed as preliminary steps toward this objective. We next prove (where (O) denotes the origin in each case):

(5.2) *Any mapping $f(x)$ of a (punctured) complex plane $X - (O)$ into another such punctured plane $W - (O)$ is homotopic [on $X - (O)$ rel. $W - (O)$] to the mapping $w = x^n$ for some integer $n = 0, \pm 1, \pm 2, \cdots$.*

Proof. Let Z be another complex plane with s- and t-axes so that $z = s + it$, and let Z_0 be the region $-\infty < s < \infty$, $-\pi \leq t \leq \pi$ of Z. The function $x = e^z$ then maps Z_0 onto $X - (O)$ continuously. Accordingly $f(e^z)$ is a mapping of Z_0 into $W - (O)$. Hence by (1.2) this mapping has an admissible exponential representation

(i) $$f(e^z) = e^{u(z)},$$

where $u(z)$ is continuous and maps Z_0 into X. Now since $e^{s+\pi i} = e^{s-\pi i}$ for every real s so that $f(e^{s+\pi i}) = f(e^{s-\pi i})$, we have by (i)

(ii) $$u(s + \pi i) - u(s - \pi i) = 2\pi i n(s),$$

where $n(s)$ is an integer for each s. But since $n(s)$ is continuous in s on the whole s-axis and this axis is connected, $n(s)$ must be a constant n for all s.

Define: $$w(x) = u(z) - nz,$$

where $x \varepsilon X - (O)$ and $x = e^z$. Then $w(x)$ is continuous and is single valued by (ii), even though there are two values of z, namely $s + \pi i$ and $s - \pi i$, for each x on the negative real axis of X (here $s = \log |x|$). Thus by (i) and $x^n = e^{nz}$ we have

$$f(x) = e^{u(z)} = x^n e^{u(z)-nz} = x^n e^{w(x)},$$

for each x in $X - (O)$. Hence we have only to define

$$h(x, \theta) = x^n e^{(1-\theta) w(x)}, \qquad 0 \leq \theta \leq 1,$$

to obtain a continuous function in (x, θ) on $X \times I$ to $W - (O)$ reducing to $f(x)$ for $\theta = 0$ and to x^n for $\theta = 1$. Thus $f(x) \simeq x^n$ on $X - (O)$ rel. $W - (O)$.

(5.21) Corollary. *If f is a homeomorphism of $X - (O)$ into $W - (O)$, then f is homotopic either to the identity mapping x or to the reciprocal mapping $1/x$.*

For if we define

$$\zeta(t) = f(e^{it}), \qquad -\pi \leq t \leq \pi,$$

then ζ is a simple traversal of the simple closed curve $f(C)$ where C is the circle $|x| = 1$. Thus since (O), the origin in W, is necessarily within the simple closed curve $f(C)$, by (2.2) and (ii) above, we have, (taking $s = 0$ and recalling that $n(s)$ is a constant n)

$$\pm 2\pi i = \mu_{f(C)}[\zeta, (O)] = u(\pi) - u(-\pi) = 2n\pi i.$$

Accordingly, $n = \pm 1$ and the corollary is proven.

(5.22) *If f is a positive (negative) homeomorphism, f is homotopic to the identity (reciprocal).*

(5.23) *If f is any homeomorphism of the plane X into the plane W, then for any $p \, \varepsilon \, X$ we have either $f(x) - f(p) \simeq x - p$ or $f(x) - f(p) \simeq [x - p]^{-1}$ according as f is a positive or a negative homeomorphism.*

(5.3) Theorem. *If a mapping $h(y)$ of a metric space Y into itself is homotopic to the identity mapping, then for any mapping $f(x)$ of a metric space X into Y, we have*

$$f \simeq hf \quad \text{(on } X \text{ rel. } Y\text{)}.$$

Proof. By hypothesis there exists a continuous function $g(y, t)$, $y \, \varepsilon \, Y$, $0 \leq t \leq 1$, such that $g(y, 0) = y$, $g(y, 1) = h(y)$ for each $y \, \varepsilon \, Y$. Then if we define

$$k(x, t) = g[f(x), t] \qquad \text{for } x \, \varepsilon \, X, \, 0 \leq t \leq 1,$$

$k(x, t)$ is continuous in (x, t) and

$$k(x, 0) = g[f(x), 0] = f(x),$$
$$k(x, 1) = g[f(x), 1] = hf(x), \text{ for all } x \, \varepsilon \, X.$$

Whence $f \simeq hf$ on X.

Clearly the same method of proof gives

(5.31) *If $h(y)$ and $l(y)$ are mappings of Y into Z and $h \simeq l$ on Y rel. Z, then for any mapping $\phi(X) = Y$ we have*

$$h\phi \simeq l\phi \quad \text{(on } X \text{ rel. } Y\text{)}$$

where X, Y and Z are arbitrary metric spaces.

(5.4) Theorem. *If f is any mapping of a simple closed curve C into the z-plane Z and h is any positive homeomorphism of Z into itself, then for any $p \, \varepsilon \, Z - f(C)$,*

(*) $$\mu_C(f, p) = \mu_C[hf, h(p)].$$

Proof. By the notes in § 1 following the definition of index and by virtue of the fact that $f \simeq hf$ clearly implies $f - p \simeq hf - p$, we may assume that $p = 0$ (the origin). In case $h(0) = 0$ our conclusion results at once from (5.1), because by (5.22) $h(z)$ is homotopic to the identity z and thus by (5.3) f and hf are homotopic on C rel. $Z - (O)$.

If $h(0) \neq 0$ we define, $k(z) = h(z) - h(0)$. Then since $k = lh$ where l is the linear transformation $l(z) = z - h(0)$, it follows by (2.6) and (2.7) that $k(z)$ is likewise a positive homeomorphism of Z into itself; and since $k(0) = 0$, the case just treated gives

(†) $$\mu_C(f, 0) = \mu_C(kf, 0) = \mu_C(lhf, 0).$$

Thus by *Note* (iv) of § 1, since l^{-1} is a linear transformation,

$$\mu_C(lhf, 0) = \mu_C(hf, l^{-1}(0)) = \mu_C[hf, h(0)].$$

This combined with (†) gives (*) for $p = 0$ and hence the theorem is proven.

REFERENCES

In connection with the material in this chapter, particularly that dealing with the topological or circulation index, and for references to other related sources see Eilenberg [1], Kuratowski [1, 2], Morse [1], Morse and Heins [1] and Whyburn [2, 3].

VI. Differentiable Functions

1. Index near a non-zero of the derivative.

(1.1) *Let $f(z)$ be a function continuous in a region R and differentiable at a point z_0 in R. If $f'(z_0) \neq 0$, for any sufficiently small simple closed curve C enclosing z_0 we have $(1/2\pi i)\mu_C(f\zeta, w_0) = 1$, where $w_0 = f(z_0)$ and where ζ is any positive traversal of C.*

For we can write

(*) $$f(z) - w_0 = (z - z_0) \cdot [f'(z_0) - \epsilon(z)]$$

where $\lim_{z \to z_0} \epsilon(z) = 0$. If C is taken sufficiently small it will lie inside R and neither side of (*) will vanish on C. Then by *Note* (iii) of V, § 1,

$$\mu_C(f\zeta, w_0) = \mu_C(z - z_0, 0) + \mu_C[f'(z_0) - \epsilon(z), 0]$$
$$= \mu_C(z, z_0) + \mu_C[-\epsilon(z), -f'(z_0)].$$

The first term on the right is $2\pi i$ by V, (2.2); and the second term is zero for C sufficiently small by V, (1.4), since $\epsilon(C)$ lies in an arbitrarily small neighborhood of 0.

2. Measure of the image of the zeros of the derivative.

(2.1) LEMMA. *Let $f(z)$ be differentiable on a subset E of a closed square D of side a. If ϵ is any positive number, E is representable in the form*

$$E = \sum_{i=1,2,\cdots} E_i,$$

where $\sum \delta(E_i)^2 \leq 2a^2$ and where each E_i contains a point z_i such that

$$\left| \frac{f(z) - f(z_i)}{z - z_i} - f'(z_i) \right| < \epsilon \quad \text{is satisfied for all } z \, \varepsilon \, E_i.$$

Proof. For each $n > 0$ let D_n be the subdivision of D into 4^n equal closed squares. Now for each $z' \, \varepsilon \, E$ there exists an $n > 0$ and a set $E_{z'}$ which is the union of 1, 2 or 4 squares of D_n each containing z' and such that z' is interior to $E_{z'}$ and

$$\left| \frac{f(z) - f(z')}{z - z'} - f'(z') \right| < \epsilon \quad \text{for all } z \, \varepsilon \, E_{z'}.$$

By the Lindelöf Theorem, E is contained in the union of a countable number of these sets $E_{z'}$, say $E \subset \sum E_{z_i'}$. We now arrange all those squares (if any) of D_1 which appear in any of the $(E_{z_i'})$ in a sequence $S_1, S_2, \cdots, S_{n_1}$ intersecting E in $E_1, E_2, \cdots, E_{n_1}$ respectively, letting $z_1, z_2, \cdots, z_{n_1}$ be the corresponding points z_i' in each case so that $z_i \, \varepsilon \, E_i$ and $E_i \subset E_{z_i}$. Similarly, all squares of D_2 which appear in any of the $(E_{z_i'})$ but which are not contained in $\sum_1^{n_1} S_i$ are arranged in a sequence $S_{n_1+1}, \cdots, S_{n_2}$ intersecting E in $E_{n_1+1}, E_{n_1+2}, \cdots, E_{n_2}$ respectively and the corresponding points $z_{n_1+1}, \cdots, z_{n_2}$ similarly chosen. Next all squares of D_3 appearing in any of the E_{z_i} but not contained in $\sum_1^{n_2} S_i$ are ordered $S_{n_2+1}, \cdots, S_{n_3}$ intersecting E in $E_{n_2+1}, E_{n_2+2}, \cdots, E_{n_3}$, and so on indefinitely. Then clearly $E = \sum E \cdot E_{z_i} = \sum E_i$ and $\sum \delta(E_i)^2 \leq 2a^2$ by areas. Also for each i, $z_i \, \varepsilon \, E_i$ and

$$\left| \frac{f(z) - f(z_i)}{z - z_i} - f'(z_i) \right| < \epsilon \text{ for } z \, \varepsilon \, E_i \text{ since } E_i \subset E_{z_j'} \text{ where } z_j' = z_i.$$

(2.2) *If $f'(z) = 0$ for all $z \, \varepsilon \, E$, then the 2-dimensional measure of $f(E)$ is 0.*

Proof. Let $\delta > 0$ be arbitrary. Choose $\epsilon < 1/2a \sqrt{\delta/2}$ and apply lemma (2.1). Then for $z \, \varepsilon \, E_i$ we have

$$|f(z) - f(z_i)|^2 < \epsilon^2 |z - z_i|^2$$

$$\delta[f(E_i)]^2 \leq \text{l.u.b. } 4 |f(z) - f(z_i)|^2 \leq 4\epsilon^2 \delta(E_i)^2$$

$$\sum \delta[f(E_i)]^2 \leq 4\epsilon^2 \sum \delta(E_i)^2 < \frac{1}{a^2} \frac{\delta}{2} \cdot 2a^2 = \delta.$$

Since $f(E) = \sum f(E_i)$, this gives our conclusion.

(2.21) COROLLARY. *The image of the set of all zeros of the derivative of a differentiable function $f(z)$ can contain no open set in the w-plane.*

3. Index.

(3.1) THEOREM. *Let $f(z)$ be continuous inside and on a simple closed curve C with interior R and differentiable on the inverse of a dense open subset E_0 of $E = f(R + C)$. For any $p \, \varepsilon \, E - f(C)$ and any positive traversal ζ of C, we have*

$$\frac{1}{2\pi i} \mu_C(f\zeta, p) > 0.$$

Proof. Let Q_0 be the component of $E - f(C)$ containing p. As Q_0 is open in E, $Q_0 \cdot E_0$ contains a region Q in E and $f^{-1}(Q)$ is open in R. Since then there is a component of $f^{-1}(Q)$ on which f is not constant, there is a point $z_0 \, \varepsilon \, f^{-1}(Q)$ where $f'(z_0) \neq 0$ (an easy consequence of the mean value theorem for real functions). Then from (1.1) it follows that if J is a sufficiently small circle lying with its interior I in $f^{-1}(Q)$ enclosing z_0 we will have

$$\frac{1}{2\pi i}\, \mu_J(f\zeta_0, w_0) = 1$$

for any positive traversal ζ_0 of J, where $w_0 = f(z_0)$. Then by V, (1.4), w_0 lies in a bounded component D of $W - f(J)$; and thus by V, (1.3) and (4.2) every point of D lies in $f(I)$ and hence in Q. Thus Q contains a square plus its interior. Accordingly by (2.2), Q must contain a point q such that $f'(z)$ does not vanish on the set $f^{-1}(q)$. Then $f^{-1}(q)$ must consist of a finite number of points $q_1, q_2, \cdots, q_m$ in R. Let $C_1, C_2, \cdots, C_m$ be circles enclosing q_1, $\cdots, q_m$ respectively and lying within C and such that no one C_i intersects any other or the interior of any other C_j and small enough so that [see (1.1)],

$$(1/2\pi i)\mu_{C_i}(f\zeta, q) = 1$$

for any positive traversal ζ of C_i. Now by V, (4.21), since f does not take the value q in the elementary region between C and $C_1, \cdots, C_m$, we have

$$\frac{1}{2\pi i}\, \mu_C(f\zeta, q) = \frac{1}{2\pi i}\sum \mu_{C_j}(f\zeta, q) = m > 0.$$

Whence

$$\frac{1}{2\pi i}\, \mu_C(f\zeta, p) = m > 0 \text{ by } V, (1.3), \text{ since } p\, \varepsilon\, Q.$$

(3.2) THEOREM. *If* $w = f(z)$ *is continuous on a simple closed curve* C *and on its interior* R *and is differentiable on the inverse of a dense open subset of* $f(R + C) - f(C)$, *then* $f(R + C)$ *consists of* $f(C)$ *together with certain bounded components of* $W - f(C)$.

COROLLARY 1. *If* $|f(z)| \leq M$ *on* C, *then* $|f(z)| \leq M$ *on* $C + R$.

COROLLARY 2. *If* $f(z)$ *is continuous on* $R + C$ *and differentiable on* $R - F$ *where* F *is a finite set of points, then* $|f(z)| \leq M$ *on* C *implies* $|f(z)| \leq M$ *on* $R + C$.

Although the concepts and results developed above in this chapter and in Chapter V are valid and were proven for completely general simple closed curves and regions in the plane, a treatment limited to the very simplest cases would be entirely adequate for the applications which are to follow in this chapter. It will be noted that these are based entirely on the case of the above results in which C is a rectangle. Thus all difficulties of subdivision of regions and approximation to general curves can be avoided. For a greatly simplified development of the material thus far in the case of C a rectangle, see the appendix.

4. The differential quotient function.

Let $f(x)$ be a complex valued function defined and continuous in a region R of the complex plane. We define the function

$$h(x, y) = \frac{f(x) - f(y)}{x - y}, \qquad \text{for} \qquad x, y \, \varepsilon \, R, x \neq y;$$

$$h(x, x) = f'(x), \qquad \text{for} \qquad x \, \varepsilon \, R, \qquad \text{when } f'(x) \text{ exists at } x.$$

Thus $h(x, y)$ is defined at all points of the cartesian product space $R \times R$ except at points (x, x) of the diagonal Δ of this space where f fails to be differentiable at x. Further, $h(x, y)$ is continuous in (x, y) at all points of $R \times R - \Delta$ and is continuous in x (and in y) separately at points (x, x) of Δ where it is defined, i.e., such that $f'(x)$ exists. We note also that $h(x, y)$ is symmetric in x and y.

(4.1) THEOREM. *Let $w = f(z)$ be continuous inside and on a rectangle C and differentiable at all points of the interior R of C except at a finite set F of points. Then if K is any compact set in R and $K_0 = K - K \cdot F$, the function $h(x, y)$ is uniformly continuous on $K_0 \times K_0$.*

Proof. Let $\epsilon > 0$ be given. By uniform continuity of $h(x, y)$ on $C \times K$, there exists a $\delta > 0$ such that

$$\left| h(t, y) - h(t, y') \right| < \epsilon/2 \qquad \text{for all} \qquad t \, \varepsilon \, C \text{ and}$$

$$\text{all } y, y' \, \varepsilon \, K \quad \text{with} \quad \left| y - y' \right| < \delta.$$

Now let (x_1, y_1), $(x_2, y_2) \, \varepsilon \, K_0 \times K_0$ with $\left| x_1 - x_2 \right| < \delta$ and $\left| y_1 - y_2 \right| < \delta$. We next define, for $z \, \varepsilon \, R + C$,

$$h(z) = h(z, y_1) - h(z, y_2), \qquad g(z) = h(x_2, z) - h(x_1, z).$$

Then $h(z)$ and $g(z)$ are continuous in $C + R$ and differentiable at all points of $R - F - x_1 - x_2 - y_1 - y_2$. Whence, by § 3, Corollary 2,

$$\left| h(z) \right| \leqq \max_{t \varepsilon C} \left| h(t, y_1) - h(t, y_2) \right| < \epsilon/2, \qquad \text{for all} \qquad z \, \varepsilon \, R,$$

$$\left| g(z) \right| \leqq \max_{t \varepsilon C} \left| h(x_2, t) - h(x_1, t) \right| < \epsilon/2, \qquad \text{for all} \qquad z \, \varepsilon \, R.$$

Whence, substituting x_1 in the first and y_2 in the second of these relations, and adding,

$$\epsilon > \left| h(x_1) \right| + \left| g(y_2) \right| \geqq \left| h(x_1) - g(y_2) \right|$$
$$= \left| h(x_1, y_1) - h(x_1, y_2) - h(x_2, y_2) + h(x_1, y_2) \right|$$
$$= \left| h(x_1, y_1) - h(x_2, y_2) \right|.$$

(4.2) THEOREM. *Let $w = f(z)$ be continuous in a region S and differentiable at all points of $S - F$ where F is a finite set of points. Then $h(x, y)$ is* *defined and continuous at all points (x, y) in $S \times S$. Thus $f'(x)$ exists and is continuous at all points of S.*

Let z_0 be any point in S, let C be a circle with center z_0 and lying together with its interior R in the region S. Let K be a circular disk centered at z_0 and lying in R and let $K_0 = K - K \cdot F$. Now since by (4.1), $h(x, y)$ is uniformly continuous on $K_0 \times K_0$, by a standard extension result [(see II, (2.3)] it admits a unique continuous extension to the closure of $K_0 \times K_0$ and thus to all of $K \times K$. In particular this extension is valid at the point (z_0, z_0); and since (z_0, z_0) is interior to $K \times K$, we have that

$$\lim_{z \to z_0} h(z, z_0) = \lim_{z \to z_0} \frac{f(z) - f(z_0)}{z - z_0} = f'(z_0)$$

exists. Thus since f is differentiable at z_0, $h(z_0, z_0)$ was already defined there; and $h(x, y)$ must be continuous at (z_0, z_0), since it is identical with its extension to $K \times K$ and (z_0, z_0) is interior to $K \times K$. As z_0 was an arbitrary point of S, our first conclusion follows. Also, $f'(x)$ exists at all points of S as just shown and it is continuous at all points of S because it is identical with $h(x, y)$ on the diagonal Δ of $S \times S$.

(4.21) COROLLARY. *If $w = f(z)$ is continuous in a region S and differentiable in S except possibly at the points of a closed, totally imperfect subset F of S, then $f(z)$ is differentiable and $f'(z)$ is continuous at all points of S.*

(4.3) REMOVABLE SINGULARITY THEOREM. *If $f(z)$ is bounded and differentiable on $R - z_0$, where R is a region containing the point z_0, then $\alpha = \lim_{z \to z_0} f(z)$ exists and if $f(z_0)$ is defined to be α, then $f(z)$ is differentiable at z_0.*

For if we define $g(z) = (z - z_0) f(z)$ for $z \neq z_0$ and $g(z_0) = 0$, then $g(z)$ is continuous throughout R and differentiable on $R - z_0$. Hence by (4.2), $g(z)$ is differentiable also at z_0 so that

$$\lim_{z \to z_0} \frac{g(z)}{z - z_0} = \lim_{z \to z_0} f(z) = \alpha, \qquad \text{exists.}$$

Hence if $f(z_0)$ is defined to be α, $f(z)$ is continuous throughout R and, by (4.2), it must also be differentiable in R.

(4.4) LIOUVILLE'S THEOREM. *If $f(z)$ is bounded and differentiable in the whole plane Z, then $f(z)$ is constant in Z.*

For let z_0 be any point whatever in Z. Then if for any $r > 0$, C is a rectangle enclosing the circle $|z - z_0| = r$, since $h(z, z_0)$ is differentiable in Z, we have

$$\left| h(z_0, z_0) \right| \leq \max_{t \varepsilon C} \left| h(t, z_0) \right| = \max_{t \varepsilon C} \left| \frac{f(t) - f(z_0)}{t - z_0} \right| \leq \frac{2M}{r},$$

$$\text{where} \quad \left| f(z) \right| \leq M \quad \text{in} \quad Z.$$

Hence $f'(z_0) = h(z_0, z_0) = 0$ for all z_0 in Z, as r can be arbitrarily large. Accordingly $f(z)$ must be constant.

5. The second derivative.

(5.1) THEOREM. *If $f(z)$ is differentiable in a region R so also is $f'(z)$.*

Proof. Let y_0 be any point of R. Then since the function $h(x, y_0)$ is continuous (in x) everywhere in R and differentiable (in x) at all points of $R - y_0$, by (4.2) it is also differentiable at y_0. Whence

$$(*) \qquad h'_x(y_0, y_0) = \lim_{x \to y_0} \frac{h(x, y_0) - h(y_0, y_0)}{x - y_0} = \lim_{x \to y_0} \frac{\dfrac{f(x) - f(y_0)}{x - y_0} - f'(y_0)}{x - y_0}.$$

Thus since for $x \neq y_0$,

$$h'_x(x, y_0) = \frac{f'(x)(x - y_0) - [f(x) - f(y_0)]}{(x - y_0)^2}$$

and since

$$\frac{f'(x) - f'(y_0)}{x - y_0} = \frac{f'(x) - \dfrac{f(x) - f(y_0)}{x - y_0}}{x - y_0} + \frac{\dfrac{f(x) - f(y_0)}{x - y_0} - f'(y_0)}{x - y_0},$$

we have

$$\lim_{x \to y_0} \frac{f'(x) - f'(y_0)}{x - y_0} = \lim_{x \to y_0} h'_x(x, y_0) + \lim_{x \to y_0} \frac{\dfrac{f(x) - f(y_0)}{x - y_0} - f'(y_0)}{x - y_0}$$

$$= h'_x(y_0, y_0) + h'_x(y_0, y_0) = 2h'_x(y_0, y_0)$$

by continuity of $h'_x(x, y_0)$ as given in (4.2) and by (*) above. Accordingly $f''(y_0)$ exists and equals $2h'_x(y_0, y_0)$.

Thus we have the classical result that the existence of the first derivative in a region implies the existence and continuity of derivatives of all orders for a function of a complex variable.

6. Higher derivatives. Order at a point.

(6.1) LEMMA. *Let $f(z)$ be differentiable in a region R containing the origin. If for $n > 0$ we have $f(0) = f'(0) = f''(0) \cdots = f^{(n-1)}(0) = 0$, then $\lim_{z \to 0} \dfrac{f(z)}{z^n}$ exists and equals $\dfrac{f^{(n)}(0)}{n!}$.*

Proof. By induction on n. For $n = 1$ this follows from $f'(0) = \lim_{z \to 0} (f(z)/z)$. Suppose it holds for $n \leq k$ and that $f(0) = f'(0) \cdots = f^{(k)}(0) = 0$. Then

$$\lim_{z \to 0} \frac{f(z)}{z^k} = \frac{f^{(k)}(0)}{k!} = 0.$$

Now define

$$h(z) = \frac{f(z)}{z^k} \quad \text{for} \quad z \neq 0,$$

$$= 0 \quad \text{for} \quad z = 0.$$

Then $h(z)$ is continuous in R (since $\lim_{z \to 0} h(z) = h(0)$) and differentiable for $z \neq 0$. Thus it is differentiable also at $z = 0$. Whence

(i) $$h'(0) = \lim_{z \to 0_-} \frac{f(z)/z^k}{z} = \lim_{z \to 0} \frac{f(z)}{z^{k+1}}.$$

Also since $0 = [f'(z)]'_{z=0} = [f'(z)]''_{z=0} = \cdots = [f'(z)]^{(k-1)}_{z=0}$, we have

(ii) $$\lim_{z \to 0} \frac{f'(z)}{z^k} = \frac{[f'(z)]^{(k)}_{z=0}}{k!} = \frac{f^{(k+1)}(0)}{k!}.$$

Further, by continuity of $h'(z)$ at $z = 0$ we get

(iii) $$h'(0) = \lim_{z \to 0} h'(z) = \lim_{z \to 0} \frac{z^k f'(z) - k z^{k-1} f(z)}{z^{2k}}$$

$$= \lim_{z \to 0} \frac{f'(z)}{z^k} - \lim_{z \to 0} \frac{k f(z)}{z^{k+1}}.$$

Thus by (i), (ii), and (iii) we get

$$(k+1) \lim_{z \to 0} \frac{f(z)}{z^{k+1}} = \lim_{z \to 0} \frac{f'(z)}{z^k} = \frac{f^{(k+1)}(0)}{k!}$$

or

$$\lim_{z \to 0} \frac{f(z)}{z^{k+1}} = \frac{f^{(k+1)}(0)}{(k+1)!},$$

which is our conclusion for $n = k + 1$.

(6.2) THEOREM. *Let $f(z)$ be differentiable in a region R. If for some point $a \varepsilon R$, $0 = f'(a) = f''(a) = \cdots$, (all derivatives of f vanish at a) then f is constant in R.*

Proof. Suppose first that $a = 0 = f(a)$. Let the circle $C: |z| = r$ be chosen so that a circumscribed square D of it lies together with its interior in R. By (6.1), $\lim_{z \to 0} (f(z)/z^n) = 0$ for all n and the function $h(z) = f(z)/z^n$ for $z \neq 0$, $h(0) = 0$, is differentiable in R. Thus for any n and all z inside C,

$$|h(z)| \leq \max_{t \varepsilon D} |h(t)| \leq \max_{t \varepsilon D} \left| \frac{f(t)}{t^n} \right| \leq \frac{M}{r^n}$$

where $M = \max_{t \varepsilon D} |f(t)|$. Thus $|f(z)| \leq M|z/r|^n$ so that $f(z) \equiv 0$ for $|z| < r$.

Now in general, applying the case just handled to the function $g(z) = f(a + z) - f(a)$, we conclude that $f(a + z) \equiv f(a)$ for $|z| < r$. Thus $f(z)$ is constant in a circular neighborhood of $z = a$. Since R is connected, f must be constant throughout R. For if R_a is the set of all points $x \, \varepsilon \, R$ such that $f(z) \equiv f(a)$ in some circular neighborhood of x, R_a is open in R by definition; and if b is any limit point of R_a in R, all derivatives of f likewise vanish at b so that $f(x) \equiv f(a)$ in a neighborhood of b. Hence R_a is also closed in R.

(6.3) *Let $f(z)$ be non-constant and differentiable in a region R, let $a \, \varepsilon \, R$ and let n be the least positive integer such that $f^{(n)}(a) \neq 0$. Then*

$$f(z) - f(a) = (z - a)^n \phi(z),$$

where $\phi(z)$ is differentiable in R and $\phi(a) \neq 0$.

For by (6.1), if $\phi(z) = (f(z) - f(a))/(z - a)^n$ for $z \neq a$ and $\phi(a) = f^n(a)/n!$, $\lim\limits_{z \to a} \phi(z) = \phi(a)$ so that our conclusion follows.

Note. The integer n is usually called the *order* or *local degree* of f at the point a.

(6.4) *If $f(z)$ is non-constant and differentiable in a region R, for any $a \, \varepsilon \, R$ we have $f(z) \neq f(a)$ for all $z \neq a$ in a sufficiently small neighborhood of a.*

7. Lightness and openness. Applications.

A mapping $f(X) = Y \subset W$ is *light* if $f^{-1}(y)$ is totally disconnected for each $y \, \varepsilon \, Y$, and is *open* (resp. *strongly open*) if $f(U)$ is open in Y (resp. W) for each open set U in X.

(7.1) THEOREM. *If $f(z)$ is non-constant and differentiable in a region R, f is light and strongly open in R.*

By (6.4) each point of $f^{-1}(y)$ is an isolated point of $f^{-1}(y)$, for any $y \, \varepsilon \, f(R)$. Hence f is surely light. Now to prove openness, let U be any open set in R and let $w_0 \, \varepsilon \, f(U)$ and $z_0 \, \varepsilon \, U \cdot f^{-1}(w_0)$. Then if C is a circle with center z_0 lying together with its interior I in U and such that $f(z) \neq w_0$ on C, by (3.2) $f(C + I)$, and therefore also $f(U)$, contains the complementary domain of $f(C)$ to which w_0 belongs. Accordingly $f(U)$ is open in the w-plane so that f is strongly open on R.

(7.11) COROLLARY (Maximum modulus theorem). *If $|f(x)| \leq M$ on the boundary $Fr(O)$ of a bounded open set O, then $|f(z)| < M$ for all $z \, \varepsilon \, O$ (given $f(z)$ non-constant and continuous on $\bar{O}$ and differentiable in O).*

Let $w = f(z)$ be analytic and non-constant in an open set R of the complex plane. We define $m(z) = |f(z)|$, $z \, \varepsilon \, R$, and call $m(z)$ the *modulus function*. Obviously it is continuous. As an immediate consequence of the strong openness of $f(z)$ on R we have

Theorem. *The mapping $m(z)$ of R into the non-negative real axis is strongly open.*

This yields at once the following for the most part standard results.

(1) *For any $a \, \varepsilon \, R$ and any neighborhood V of a in R, there exists $z \, \varepsilon \, V$ such that $m(z) > m(a)$; and if $m(a) \neq 0$, there exists $z_1 \, \varepsilon \, V$ such that $m(z_1) < m(a)$.*

(2) *$m(z)$ has no relative weak maximum points and no relative weak minimum points other than zeros.*

Note. For real valued functions on R the absence of relative maximum and minimum points implies strong openness.

(3) Maximum Modulus Theorem. *If $f(z)$ is analytic in a bounded open set G and continuous on $Fr(G)$ and $\big|f(z)\big| \leqq M$ on $Fr(G)$, then $\big|f(z)\big| < M$ for $z \, \varepsilon \, G$.*

For otherwise, by (1), $m(z)$ exceeds M for some $z \, \varepsilon \, G$. Then $m(a) = \max_{z \varepsilon \bar{G}} m(z)$ for some $a \, \varepsilon \, G$, which is impossible by (1).

(4) *If $f(z)$ is analytic in a bounded open set G complementary to a level curve $L : \big|f(z)\big| = k$ and continuous on $Fr(G)$ where $Fr(G) \subset L$, $f(z)$ has at least one zero in G.*

For by (3), $\big|f(z)\big| < k$ on G. Thus $m(a) = \min_{z \varepsilon \bar{G}} m(z)$ for some $a \, \varepsilon \, G$; and by (1), $m(a)$ must be 0.

(5) *Every (non-constant) polynomial has at least one zero.*

For let $w_0 \neq 0$ be a value of a polynomial $P(z)$. The open set G defined by $\big|P(z)\big| < \big|w_0\big|$ is bounded, since $P(z) \to \infty$ as $z \to \infty$, and $Fr(G)$ is contained in the level curve $\big|P(z)\big| = \big|w_0\big|$. Thus the result follows from (4).

(6) *Let R be any bounded region with connected boundary B and let $f(z)$ be analytic on R and continuous on B. Then either $m(R) \subset m(B)$ or else f has at least one zero in R.*

For the set $m(B)$ is a continuum and hence is an interval $\alpha \leqq x \leqq \beta$ of the non-negative real axis; and if it does not contain $m(R)$, we have $\alpha > m(z_0) > 0$ for some $z_0 \, \varepsilon \, R$ by (3). Thus $m(a) = \min_{z \varepsilon R} m(z)$ for some $a \, \varepsilon \, R$ and $m(a) = 0$ by (1).

8. The Cauchy Inequality. Power series expansion.

In view of the Removable Singularity Theorem we can now state the maximum principle in the form

(8.1) Maximum Principle. *If $f(z)$ is continuous on a simple closed curve C and is bounded and differentiable on $G - F$ where G is the interior of C and F is a finite set in G, then $\big|f(z)\big| \leqq M$ on C implies $\big|f(z)\big| \leqq M$ also on G.*

This holds in particular if $f(z)$ is continuous on C, differentiable on $G - F$ and $\lim\limits_{z \to z_0} f(z)$ exists and is finite for each $z_0 \, \varepsilon \, F$. Further, these two forms of the condition are equivalent and f is actually differentiable also at each $z_0 \, \varepsilon \, F$ when suitably defined there.

(8.2) CAUCHY INEQUALITY. *Given $f(z)$ differentiable in $|z| < R$. Then for any $r < R$ and any n*

$$\frac{\left| f^{(n)}(0) \right|}{n!} r^n \leqq M(r), \tag{*}$$

where $M(r) = \max\limits_{|z|=r} \left| f(z) \right|$.

Proof. Define the function

$$g(z) = \sum_{0}^{2n-1} (-1)^k f(zw^k), \text{ where } w = e^{i\pi/n}$$

Then, $g(0) = f(0) \sum_{k=0}^{2n-1} (-1)^k = 0$, and also for $1 \leqq j < n$,

$$g^{(j)}(0) = \sum_{k=0}^{2n-1} (-1)^k w^{jk} f^{(j)}(0) = f^{(j)}(0) \frac{1 - w^{2nj}}{1 + w^j} = 0.$$

In addition,

$$g^{(n)}(0) = \sum_{k=0}^{2n-1} (-1)^k (w^n)^k f^{(n)}(0) = f^{(n)}(0) \sum_{0}^{2n-1} (-1)^{2k} = 2n f^{(n)}(0).$$

Thus, by (6.1), $\lim\limits_{z \to 0} g(z)/z^n$ exists and equals $g^{(n)}(0)/n! = 2n f^{(n)}(0)/n!$. Hence by the maximum principle, (8.1) above,

$$2n \frac{\left| f^{(n)}(0) \right|}{n!} \leqq \operatorname*{Max}_{|z|=r} \frac{\left| g(z) \right|}{r^n} \leqq 2n \operatorname*{Max}_{|z|=r} \frac{\left| f(z) \right|}{r^n} = \frac{2n M(r)}{r^n}.$$

This is equivalent to (*).

(8.3) THEOREM (Maclaurin's development): *Let $f(z)$ be differentiable in $|z| < R$. Then the series $\sum_0^\infty a_n z^n$ converges to $f(z)$ uniformly in any disk $|z| \leqq \rho$ for any $\rho < R$, where $a_n = f^{(n)}(0)/n!$.*

Proof. With ρ given, let r be chosen so that $\rho < r < R$. By the Cauchy inequality, we have

$$\left| a_n \right| r^n \leqq M(r) \qquad \text{for all } n. \tag{i}$$

Thus, if we define, for $|z| < R$,

$$h(z) = f(z) - \sum_{0}^{n-1} a_k z^k, \tag{ii}$$

we have

$$\left| h(z) \right| \leqq (n+1) M(r), \quad \text{for} \quad |z| \leqq r, \quad \text{by (i) and (8.1).} \tag{iii}$$

Now since it is readily verified that

$$0 = h(0) = h'(0) = h''(0) = \cdots = h^{(n-1)}(0),$$

it follows by (6.1) that $\lim\limits_{z \to 0} h(z)/z^n$ exists and equals $f^{(n)}(0)/n!$. Hence by (8.1), for any z with $|z| \leq \rho$, $z \neq 0$,

$$\frac{h(z)}{z^n} \leq \operatorname*{Max}_{|z|=r} \frac{|h(z)|}{r^n} \leq (n+1)\, \frac{M(r)}{r^n},$$

by (iii). Whence $|h(z)| \leq M(r)(n+1)/(r/\rho)^n$ for $|z| \leq \rho$, and the right-hand member here converges to 0 as $n \to \infty$ since $r/\rho > 1$. Thus, given $\epsilon > 0$, for $n > N$, $|h(z)| < \epsilon$ for all z with $|z| \leq \rho$, which is our conclusion.

VII. Degree. Zeros. Sequences

1. Local topological analysis. Degree.

For convenience we define the *winding number* $w_c(f, p)$ of a mapping f on a simple closed curve C into a plane Z about a point p of $Z - f(C)$ by

$$w_c(f, p) = \frac{1}{2\pi i}\, \mu_c(f, p)$$

Let $f(z)$ be non-constant and differentiable in a region R. As noted in (6.3) for each $a \,\varepsilon\, R$ the least positive integer k_a such that $f^{(k_a)}(a) \neq 0$ is the *local degree* of f at a. In particular $k_a = 1$ if $f'(a) \neq 0$.

(1.1) THEOREM. *For any sufficiently small simple closed curve C lying in R and enclosing a, we have*

$$w_c[f, f(a)] = k_a.$$

Proof. By (6.3) we have the representation

$$f(z) - f(a) = (z - a)^{k_a}\phi(z), \qquad z \,\varepsilon\, R,$$

where $\phi(z)$ is differentiable in R and $\phi(a) \neq 0$. Now let C be taken small enough so that if I is its interior, then $C + I$ lies in R and the origin of the w plane W lies in the unbounded component of $W - \phi(C + I)$. Then $w_c(\phi, 0) = 0$ so that by results in Chapter V, we get

$$w_c[f, f(a)] = w_c[f(z) - f(a), 0] = w_c[(z - a)^{k_a}, 0] + w_c(\phi, 0)$$

$$= w_c[(z - a)^{k_a}, 0]$$

$$= k_a w_c(z - a, 0)$$

$$= k_a w_c(z, a) = k_a$$

since $w_c(z, a) = 1$.

(1.11) $f'(a) \neq 0$ *if and only if* $k_a = 1$. *Also* $f(z)$ *generates a local homeomorphism at* a *if* $f'(a) \neq 0$ (*or* $k_a = 1$).

To see the latter, we have only to note that if $f'(a) = h(a, a) \neq 0$, then $h(x, y) \neq 0$ in a neighborhood $U \times U$ of (a, a) where U is a neighborhood of a in R. Thus $\dfrac{f(x) - f(y)}{x - y} \neq 0$ for all x, $y \,\varepsilon\, U$ with $x \neq y$.

(1.2) THEOREM. $f(z)$ *is locally topologically equivalent at a to the power mapping* $w = z^{k_a}$. *Thus for a suitably chosen topological disk* D *enclosing a we have* $f(z) - f(a) = [s(z)]^{k_a}$ *for* $z \varepsilon D$, *where* $s(z)$ *is a homeomorphism on* D.

Proof. Let $f(z) - f(a) = (z - a)^{k_a}\phi(z)$, where $\phi(a) \neq 0$, and ϕ is differentiable in R. Consider the function

$$s(z) = (z - a)\phi(z)^{1/k_a}.$$

Since $s'(z) = \phi(z)^{1/k_a} + (1/k_a)\phi(z)^{1/k_a-1}\phi'(z)(z - a)$, so that $s'(a) = \phi(a)^{1/k_a} \neq 0$, s generates a local homeomorphism of Z into the complex plane S in the neighborhood of a. Now the function

$$w = g(s) = s^{k_a} = (z - a)^{k_a}\phi(z) = f(z) - f(a),$$

is a power function in the neighborhood of $s = 0$. Thus $f(z) - f(a)$ factors into the form

$$f(z) - f(a) = g[s(z)] = [(z - a)\phi(z)^{1/k_a}]^{k_a},$$

where $s(z)$ is a homeomorphism in a neighborhood of a and g is a power mapping of degree k_a.

(1.21) COROLLARY. *For any* $z \varepsilon D - a$, *there are exactly* k_a *distinct points of* $f^{-1}f(z)$ *on* D. *In particular, f is a local homeomorphism at a if and only if* $k_a = 1$ *(or $f'(a) \neq 0$).*

(1.22) COROLLARY. *At any point a in* R, *local degree = local multiplicity = winding number at a.*

DEFINITION. For any $y \varepsilon f(R)$, the sum $k(y)$ (finite or infinite) of the local degrees of f at all points of $R \cdot f^{-1}(y)$ will be called the *degree of f at y.*

(1.3) THEOREM. *Let $f(z)$ be continuous on a simple closed curve C and differentiable on the interior R of C. For any component Q of $f(R + C) - f(C)$, $k(y)$ is finite and constant on Q. Indeed we have*

$$k(y) = w_c(f, y) = k, \qquad \text{for} \qquad \text{all } y \varepsilon Q.$$

This is an immediate consequence of (1.22) together with the results in Chapter V, § 1.

(1.31) COROLLARY. *On $R \cdot f^{-1}(Q)$, f is compact and of constant degree. For any $p \varepsilon Q$, the number of p-places (each counted with multiplicity) of f in R is constant and* $= w_c(f, p)$.

(1.32) COROLLARY. *If $f(z) \neq 0$ on C, there are exactly $w_c(f, 0)$ zeros of f within C.*

2. Rouché's Theorem.　Zeros and poles.

As would be expected, other standard results on zeros and poles are immediate consequences of this sequence of conclusions.

(2.1) ROUCHÉ'S THEOREM. *If $f(z)$ and $g(z)$ are continuous and differenti-able within and on a simple closed curve C and $|g(z)| < |f(z)|$ on C, then $f(z)$ and $f(z) + g(z)$ have the same number of zeros within C.*

This is a direct consequence of (1.31) above, together with V, (3.12). We need only take p as the origin and let $f_1(z) = f(z) + g(f)$.

DEFINITIONS. A point p is called a *pole* of a function $w = f(z)$ provided f is finite and differentiable at all points of $U - p$ for some open set U about p and $\lim_{z \to p} f(z) = \infty$. The function $w = f(z)$ is said to be *mero-morphic* in a region R provided it is differentiable at all points of R except for poles.

(2.2) *If z_0 is a pole of a function $f(z)$, there exists a region R about z_0 and an integer $k > 0$ such that*

$$f(z) = (z - z_0)^{-k}\phi(z), \qquad \text{for } z \varepsilon R,$$

where $\phi(z)$ is differentiable and $\neq 0$ throughout R.

In this case z_0 is said to be a pole of *order k* of f. To see this we take a region U about z_0 so that $f(z) \neq 0$ in U and define

$$g(z) = 1/f(z), \qquad z \varepsilon U - z_0,$$

$$g(z_0) = 0.$$

Then $\lim_{z \to z_0} g(z) = 0$ so that by the results in Chapter VI, g is differentiable throughout U. Thus by VI, (6.3) there is an integer $k > 0$ and a differenti-able function $\varphi(z)$ in U with $\varphi(z_0) \neq 0$ so that

$$g(z) = (z - z_0)^k\varphi(z), \qquad z \varepsilon U.$$

This gives $f(z) = (z - z_0)^{-k}\phi(z)$, where $\phi(z) = \dfrac{1}{\varphi(z)}$, and this relation holds in any region R in U about z_0 taken so that $\varphi(z) \neq 0$ in R.

(2.3) THEOREM. *If $f(z)$ is meromorphic on a region containing the simple closed curve C and its interior and is finite and $\neq 0$ on C, then*

(i) $$w_c(f, 0) = N - P,$$

where N and P are the numbers of zeros and poles respectively inside C (each counted with its order or multiplicity).

Proof. Let C_0 and C_p be disjoint simple closed curves inside C en-closing all zeros and all poles, respectively, of f inside C and such that their interiors are disjoint. Then since f is finite and $\neq 0$ on the closed ele-mentary region R bounded by C, C_0, and C_p,

(ii) $$w_c(f, 0) = w_{C_0}(f, 0) + w_{C_p}(f, 0).$$

Now if we define $g(z) = 1/f(z)$ for z on or inside C_p, it follows by (2.2) and (1.31) that

$$w_{C_p}(g, 0) = \text{number of zeros of } g \text{ inside } C_p$$
$$= \text{number of poles of } f \text{ inside } C_p$$
$$= P.$$

However, this gives $w_{C_p}(f, 0) = -P$ since $f \cdot g = 1$ on C_p so that $w_c(f, 0) + w_c(g, 0) = w_c(1, 0) = 0$. This, together with (ii) gives (i), since $w_{C_0}(f, 0) = N$ by (1.31).

3. Termwise differentiability.

A sequence of functions in a region R which converge uniformly on each compact set in R is said to converge *almost uniformly* in R. Using only the results in VI, §§ 1–4, we now establish the standard result.

(3.1) THEOREM. *If the sequence of differentiable functions $[f_n(z)]$ in a region R converges almost uniformly to $f(z)$ in R, then $f(z)$ is differentiable in R and the sequence $[f'_n(z)]$ converges almost uniformly to $f'(z)$ in R.*

Proof. Let M be any compact set in R. We shall now show that the sequence of corresponding differential quotient functions $h_n(x, y)$ converge uniformly on $M \times M$. Let O be a bounded open set such that $M \subset O \subset \bar{O} \subset R$ and let r be the distance from M to the boundary $\mathrm{Fr}(O)$ of O. Then if $\epsilon > 0$ there exists an N such that

(i) $\left| f_n(t) - f_m(t) \right| < r\epsilon/2,$ for all $t \, \varepsilon \, \bar{O}$ and $m, n > N.$

Now for any fixed $y \, \varepsilon \, M$ we have, for all $x \, \varepsilon \, M$,

(ii) $\left| h_n(x, y) - h_m(x, y) \right| \leq \max_{t \varepsilon \mathrm{Fr}(O)} \left| h_n(t, y) - h_m(t, y) \right|$

$$= \max_{t \varepsilon \mathrm{Fr}(O)} \left| \frac{f_n(t) - f_n(y)}{t - y} - \frac{f_m(t) - f_m(y)}{t - y} \right|$$

$$\leq \frac{1}{r} \max_{t \varepsilon \mathrm{Fr}(O)} \left| f_n(t) - f_m(t) + f_m(y) - f_n(y) \right|$$

$$\leq \frac{1}{r} \max_{t \varepsilon \mathrm{Fr}(O)} \left[\left| f_n(t) - f_m(t) \right| + \left| f_n(y) - f_m(y) \right| \right]$$

$$< \frac{1}{r} \cdot 2 \frac{r\epsilon}{2} = \epsilon \qquad \text{by (i)}.$$

Thus for all $x, y \, \varepsilon \, M$, i.e., $(x, y) \, \varepsilon \, M \times M$,

$$\left| h_n(x, y) - h_m(x, y) \right| < \epsilon \qquad \text{for} \qquad m, n > N,$$

so that $h_n(x, y)$ converges uniformly on $M \times M$.

Now in particular $h_n(x, y)$ converges uniformly on the set $\Delta \cdot M \times M$ and on this set $h_n(z, z) \equiv f_n'(z)$. Thus $f_n'(z)$ converges uniformly on M and hence converges almost uniformly on R.

Now let $g(x, y) = \lim_{n \to \infty} h_n(x, y)$ for $(x, y) \; \varepsilon \; R \times R$. Then $g(x, y)$ is continuous in $R \times R$; and for $x_0 \neq y_0$ we have

$$g(x_0, y_0) = \lim_{n \to \infty} h_n(x_0, y_0) = \frac{1}{x_0 - y_0} \left[\lim_{n \to \infty} f_n(x_0) - \lim_{n \to \infty} f_n(y_0) \right]$$

$$= \frac{1}{x_0 - y_0} [f(x_0) - f(y_0)] = h(x_0, y_0).$$

Thus if $z_0 \; \varepsilon \; R$, continuity of $g(x, y)$ gives $\lim_{z \to z_0} g(z, z_0) = g(z_0, z_0)$ so that $\lim_{z \to z_0} h(z, z_0) = g(z_0, z_0)$, since $g(z, z_0) \equiv h(z, z_0)$ for $z \neq z_0$. Thus $\lim_{z \to z_0} \dfrac{f(z) - f(z_0)}{z - z_0}$ exists and equals $g(z_0, z_0)$. Hence $f'(z_0)$ exists and equals $g(z_0, z_0)$; and this concludes the proof of the theorem since we already have shown that $f_n'(z)$ converges almost uniformly to $g(z_0, z_0) = f'(z_0)$.

This result yields an interesting second proof for the

THEOREM. *If $f(z)$ is differentiable in a region R, so also is $f'(z)$.* (VI, § 5 above.)

For let $z_0 \; \varepsilon \; R$ and let C be a circle with center z_0 and lying with its interior I in R. Then if a_n is any sequence of non-zero numbers converging to 0 and with $z + a_n \subset R$ for $z \; \varepsilon \; I$, each of the functions $h(z + a_n, z)$ is differentiable in I. Also by uniform continuity of $h(x, y)$, the sequence $[h(z + a_n, z)]$ converges uniformly to $f'(z)$ on I. Thus by (3.1), $f'(z)$ is itself differentiable on I.

4. Hurwitz's Theorem.

Let the sequence of functions $f_n(z)$, each differentiable in a region R, converge uniformly in R to a function $f(z)$ not identically zero. Then if $\zeta \; \varepsilon \; R$ is an m-fold zero of $f(z)$, every sufficiently small neighborhood D of ζ contains exactly m zeros of $f_n(z)$ for $n > N(D)$.

For let C be a circle in R about ζ containing no zero of $f(z)$ and whose interior D lies in R and contains no zero of $f(z)$ other than ζ. Since $f(z) \neq 0$ on C, there exists an integer $N(D)$ such that if $n > N(D)$, $|f_n(z) - f(z)| < |f(z)|$ for all $z \; \varepsilon \; C$. Then since $f(z)$ is differentiable in R by § 3 so that (2.1) applies, it follows that $f(z)$ and $f_n(z)$ have the same number, m, of zeros inside C.

5. The Vitali Theorems.

We begin with a series of "Ascoli-type" theorems valid in a general topological setting. Let X and Y be separable metric spaces. A family

$\mathscr{F}$ of transformations of X into Y is *equicontinuous* at $a \, \varepsilon \, X$ provided that for any $\epsilon > 0$ a $\delta_a > 0$ exists such that $\rho[f(x), f(a)] < \epsilon$ for any $f \, \varepsilon \, \mathscr{F}$ provided $\rho(x, a) < \delta_a$. Similarly, $\mathscr{F}$ is equicontinuous on a set A in X provided it is equicontinuous at each $a \, \varepsilon \, A$ and is *equiuniformly continuous* on A provided that for any $\epsilon > 0$ a $\delta > 0$ exists such that $\rho[f(a_1), f(a_2)] < \epsilon$ for any $f \, \varepsilon \, \mathscr{F}$ provided $a_1, a_2 \, \varepsilon \, A$ and $\rho(a_1, a_2) < \delta$.

(5.1) *If $\mathscr{F}$ is equicontinuous on X, it is equiuniformly continuous on each compact set A in X.*

For if not, then for some $\epsilon > 0$ there would exist a point $a \, \varepsilon \, A$ and two sequences (b_n) and (c_n) of points in A each converging to a and such that, for each n, there exists $f_n \, \varepsilon \, \mathscr{F}$ such that $\rho[f_n(b_n), f_n(c_n)] \geqq \epsilon$. However, by equicontinuity of $\mathscr{F}$ at a, for n sufficiently large b_n and c_n would be close enough to a so that $\rho[f_n(b_n), f_n(a)] < \epsilon/2$ and $\rho[f_n(c_n), f_n(a)] < \epsilon/2$; and by the triangle inequality these give $\rho[f_n(b_n), f_n(c_n)] < \epsilon$, a contradiction.

(5.2) *If X is locally compact, and Y is complete, any equicontinuous sequence $[f_n(x)]$ of mappings of X into Y which converges pointwise on a dense subset X_0 of X converges almost uniformly on X.*

Proof. For each $x \, \varepsilon \, X_0$ let $f(x) = \lim_{n \to \infty} f_n(x)$. Let E be any compact set in X and let $\epsilon > 0$ be given. By local compactness of X, E is interior to a compact set E_0 in X. By (5.1) our sequence is equiuniformly continuous on E_0. Let $\delta > 0$ be chosen $< \rho(E, X - E_0)$ and also so that $\rho[f_n(a_1), f_n(a_2)] < \epsilon/4$ for each n and each $a_1, a_2 \, \varepsilon \, E_0$ with $\rho(a_1, a_2) < \delta$. Since X_0 is dense in X there exists a finite set of points $x_1, x_2, \cdots, x_k \, \varepsilon$ $X_0 \cdot E_0$ such that any $x \, \varepsilon \, E$ is at distance $< \delta$ from some x_i. Also by pointwise convergence on X_0, there exists an integer N such that for any $n > N$ and any $i \leqq k$,

(*) $$\rho[f_n(x_i), f(x_i)] < \epsilon/4$$

Now take any $x \, \varepsilon \, E$. Choose i so that $\rho(x, x_i) < \delta$. Then for any $m, n > N$ we have

$$\rho[f_n(x), f_n(x_i)] < \epsilon/4, \qquad \text{(by equiuniform continuity on } E_0\text{)}$$

$$\rho[f_n(x_i), f(x_i)] < \epsilon/4, \qquad \text{by (*)}$$

Similarly

$$\rho[f(x_i), f_m(x_i)] < \epsilon/4 \quad \text{and}$$

$$\rho[f_m(x_i), f_m(x)] < \epsilon/4.$$

Accordingly, $\rho[f_n(x), f_m(x)] < \epsilon$ by the triangle inequality.

(5.3) *Any infinite sequence of mappings of X into Y which is bounded (i.e., has a conditionally compact set of values) at each point of X contains an infinite subsequence which converges at each point of a dense subset of X.*

For let $P = \sum p_n$ be dense in X and let (f_n) be the given sequence. Then choose an infinite subsequence $(f_{1n}) = f_{11}, f_{12}, \cdots$ of (f_n) with terms written down in the same order as before and which is convergent at p_1. Next choose a similar subsequence $(f_{2n}) = f_{21}, f_{22}, \cdots$ of (f_{1n}) which converges at p_2, a subsequence $(f_{3n}) = f_{31}, f_{32}, \cdots$ of (f_{2n}) convergent at p_3, and so on. It is then clear that the diagonal sequence $(f_{nn}) = f_{11}, f_{22}, f_{33}, \cdots$ will converge at each of the points p_n of P.

(5.4) THEOREM (Ascoli). *If X is locally compact and Y is complete, any infinite equicontinuous sequence of mappings of X into Y which has a conditionally compact set of values at each point of X contains an infinite subsequence which converges almost uniformly on X.*

For by (5.3) any such sequence contains an infinite subsequence (f_n) which converges at each point of an everywhere dense subset X_0 of X. The sequences (f_n) is itself equicontinuous and thus our conclusion follows directly from (5.2).

Now consider a family $\mathscr{F}$ of functions each differentiable in a region R of the complex plane.

(5.5) THEOREM. *Any family $\mathscr{F}$ of differentiable functions in a region R which is uniformly bounded on each compact set in R is equicontinuous in R.*

For let $z_0 \, \varepsilon \, R$ and let $\epsilon > 0$ be given. Choose $r > 0$ so that the disk $D \colon |z - z_0| \leqq r$ lies wholly in R and let C be the boundary of D. By hypothesis there exists a constant M such that $|f(z)| \leqq M$ for all $f \, \varepsilon \, \mathscr{F}$ and all $z \, \varepsilon \, D$. Let us choose $\delta = \min [r, r\epsilon/2M]$.

Then if f is any function of $\mathscr{F}$ and $|z - z_0| < \delta$, we have

$$\left| h(z, z_0) \right| \leqq \underset{t \varepsilon C}{\text{Max}} \left| h(t, z_0) \right| = \underset{t \varepsilon C}{\text{Max}} \frac{|f(t) - f(z_0)|}{|t - z_0|} \leqq 2M/r.$$

Whence

$$\left| f(z) - f(z_0) \right| \leqq \frac{2M}{r} \left| z - z_0 \right| < \frac{2M}{r} \delta \leqq \frac{2M}{r} \cdot \frac{r\epsilon}{2M} = \epsilon.$$

(5.6) THEOREM. *Any infinite sequence of differentiable functions in a region R which is uniformly bounded on each compact set in R contains an infinite subsequence which converges almost uniformly in R.*

This is a direct consequence of (5.4) and (5.5).

(5.7) THEOREM (Vitali). *Let S be a sequence of differentiable functions in a region R which is uniformly bounded on each compact set in R. If S converges at each point of a set E having a limit point in R, then S converges almost uniformly throughout R.*

For by (5.6) some subsequence S_1 of S converges almost uniformly in R and by (3.1) its limit function $f(z)$ is differentiable in R. Then S itself must converge to $f(z)$ at each $z \, \varepsilon \, R$. For if not, then for some

$z_0 \, \varepsilon \, R$ there is a point $w_1 \neq f(z_0)$ which is the unique limit of $[g_n(z_0)]$ for some infinite subsequence (g_n) of S. Then again by (5.7) a subsequence of (g_n) converges almost uniformly to a function $g(z)$ differentiable in R and with $g(z_0) = w_1$.

However, since $f(z) \equiv g(z)$ for $z \, \varepsilon \, E$ we must have $f(z) \equiv g(z)$ throughout R, contrary to $g(z_0) \neq f(z_0)$. Thus S itself converges to $f(z)$ at all $z \, \varepsilon \, R$ and hence converges almost uniformly by (5.2).

VIII. Open Mappings. Local Analysis

1. General Theorems. Property S and local connectedness

We will be concerned throughout this section with a mapping $f(X) = Y$ where X and Y are separable metric spaces. It will be recalled that f is *open* provided that if U is open in X, $f(U)$ is open in Y. Also we remark that if f is open, then for any *inverse set* I in X, i.e., a set satisfying: $I = f^{-1}f(I)$, the mapping $f|I$ is an open mapping of I onto $f(I)$.

Our main objective will be to establish conditions under which local connectedness and Property S are invariant under the inverse f^{-1} of an open mapping. While neither of these properties is invariant under all mappings, it may be noted that, by II, (1.5), Property S is invariant under uniformly continuous mappings; and it is readily seen that local connectedness is invariant under any open mapping $f(X) = Y$. To exhibit this, by I, (12.1), we have only to show that, assuming X locally connected, if U is any open set in Y and R is any component of U then R is open in Y. We note, however, that $f^{-1}(R)$ is an open set since it is made up of those components of the open set $f^{-1}(U)$ which intersect $f^{-1}(R)$ and each such component is open by local connectedness of X. Thus R is open by openness of f.

(*Note:* This argument is valid assuming only that f is *quasi-compact*, i.e., the image of each open inverse set is open, rather than that f is open. Thus in particular, local connectedness is also invariant under all *closed mappings* and under all *retractions*.)

(1.1) *If X is locally compact, Y is a continuum and f is open, then any compact component of X maps onto Y.*

For let H be a compact component of X and suppose there is a point y_0 in $Y - f(H)$. Since H is compact and $H \cdot f^{-1}(y_0)$ is empty, there exists an open set V in X containing H such that $\bar{V}$ is compact and does not intersect $f^{-1}(y_0)$. Then by I, (9.3), applied to the set $\bar{V}$, there exists a separation

$$\bar{V} = V_h + V_0$$

where $H \subset V_h$ and $Fr(V) \subset V_0$. But then V_h is both open and compact. Thus $f(V_h)$ is both open and closed in Y and hence must be Y since Y is connected. This is impossible since $f(\bar{V})$ cannot contain y_0.

DEFINITION. A set E is a *semi-continuum* provided each pair of points a, $b \,\varepsilon\, E$ lie together in a continuum in E. In particular any arcwise connected set is a semi-continuum, and hence so also is any region in a locally connected generalized continuum.

(1.11) *If X is locally compact, R is any semi-continuum in Y and f is open on $f^{-1}(R)$, then any conditionally compact component Q of $f^{-1}(R)$ maps onto R.*

For let K be a continuum in R containing $y + z$, where y is any given point of R and $z = f(x_0)$ for some $x_0 \,\varepsilon\, Q$. Then $f^{-1}(K)$ is closed in X and thus is locally compact. Also the component H of $f^{-1}(K)$ containing x_0 lies in Q and thus is compact. Hence, applying (1.1) to the open mapping $f|f^{-1}(K)$ we get $f(H) = K$. Thus $f(Q) \supset f(H) \supset y$.

DEFINITION. A set P is said to be *scattered* provided no point of P is a limit point of P.

For our mapping $f(X) = Y$ we let S denote the set of all $y \,\varepsilon\, Y$ such that $f^{-1}(y)$ is a scattered set. For any set N in a space M we denote by int. N the set of all interior points of N, i.e., int. $N = N - \overline{M - N}$.

(1.2) *If X is a locally connected generalized continuum, f is open and R is a semi-continuum in Y with int. $R + R \cdot S \neq \Phi$ (Φ is the empty set), then only a finite number of components of $f^{-1}(R)$ lie in any given compact set H in X.*

For let y be a point of $R \cdot S + $ int. R. The set $K = H \cdot f^{-1}(y)$ is compact in any case and is finite in case $y \,\varepsilon\, S$. By (1.11) each component Q of $f^{-1}(R)$ lying in H must map onto R and thus itself must intersect K. Hence if $y \,\varepsilon\, S$ the number of such components Q cannot exceed the number of points in the finite set K. If $y \,\varepsilon\,$ int. R we have $y \,\varepsilon\, U \subset R$ where U is open. Thus by local connectedness of X, each $p \,\varepsilon\, K$ is interior to a component of $f^{-1}(U)$ and thus is interior to the component of $f^{-1}(R)$ to which it belongs. Thus by the Borel theorem only a finite number, say k, of components of $f^{-1}(R)$ can intersect K. Thus again the number of such components Q lying in H cannot exceed k.

(1.3) THEOREM. *If f is light and X is locally compact, then for any compact subsets H of X and K of Y and any $\epsilon > 0$, there exists a $\delta > 0$ such that for any δ-set R in Y intersecting K, each component of $f^{-1}(R)$ intersecting H is conditionally compact and of diameter $< \epsilon$.*

The conditional compactness of small components intersecting H follows from local compactness of X. Now suppose, contrary to the rest of our conclusion that for some H, K, and ϵ no such δ exists. Then there would exist a sequence $R_1, R_2, \cdots$ of subsets of Y each intersecting K and with $\delta(R_n) < 1/n$ and a sequence $Q_1, Q_2, \cdots$ of components of $f^{-1}(R_1), f^{-1}(R_2), \cdots$ respectively such that for each n, Q_n intersects H and is of diameter $\geq \epsilon$. Since H and K are compact, we may suppose the sequence $R_1, R_2, \cdots$ chosen so that it converges to a single point $p \, \varepsilon \, K$ and also suppose $Q_1, Q_2, \cdots$ chosen so that it converges to a limit set L which intersects H and thus is not empty. But by continuity of f, we must have $L \subset f^{-1}(p)$; and thus each component of L would reduce to a single point. On the other hand, since $\delta(Q_n) \geqq \epsilon$ for each n and each Q_n is connected and intersects H, it readily follows from I, § 9, that any component of L intersecting H is non-degenerate. This contradiction establishes (1.3).

(1.4) *Let X be a locally connected generalized continuum, let N be a conditionally compact generalized continuum in Y with int. $N + N \cdot S$ dense in N and suppose f is light and open. Then if N has property S so also has any conditionally compact component Q of $f^{-1}(N)$.*

Proof. Let $\epsilon > 0$ be given. Apply (1.3) for $H = \bar{Q}$, $K = \bar{N}$, thus finding δ so that any component of the inverse image of a δ-subset of $\bar{N}$ lying in $\bar{Q}$ is of diameter $< \epsilon$. Next we write

$$N = \sum_1^k N_i$$

where each N_i is a region in N of diameter $< \delta$.

Since each N_i is a semi-continuum (by local connectedness of N) with (int. $N_i + N_i \cdot S) \neq \Phi$, and since $f^{-1}(N) \cdot Q = f^{-1}(N) \cdot \bar{Q}$, as Q is closed in $f^{-1}(N)$, by (1.2) $f^{-1}(N_i) \cdot Q$ consists of a finite number of components of $f^{-1}(N_i)$, say

$$f^{-1}(N_i) \cdot Q = \sum_{j=1}^{k_i} N_i^j$$

Since $\delta(N_i^j) < \epsilon$ for each i and j and $Q = \sum_i \sum_j N_i^j$, our conclusion follows.

(1.41) COROLLARY. *Under the same conditions as in (1.4), the union of all components of $f^{-1}(N)$ lying in any compact subset of X has property S.*

(1.5) THEOREM. *Suppose X is a locally connected generalized continuum and that f is light and open. If E is any locally connected generalized continuum in Y with int. $E + E \cdot S$ dense in E, $f^{-1}(E)$ is locally connected.*

Proof. Let $x \, \varepsilon \, f^{-1}(E)$, $y = f(x)$. Let $\epsilon > 0$ be chosen so that $\overline{V_{2\epsilon}(x)}$ is compact. Then with $H = \overline{V_\epsilon(x)}$, $K = y$ determine δ from (1.3) so that any component of $f^{-1}[V_\delta(y)]$ intersecting H is of diameter $< \epsilon$. Then let R be a region in E about y lying in $V_\delta(y)$ which has property S. Then by (1.41) the union Q of all components of $f^{-1}(R)$ lying in $\overline{V_{2\epsilon}(x)}$ has property S. Also any component of $f^{-1}(R)$ intersecting $V_\epsilon(x)$ lies in Q, as it is of diameter $< \epsilon$; and since $f^{-1}(R)$ is open in $f^{-1}(E)$, x is not a limit point of $f^{-1}(E) - Q$. Thus $f^{-1}(E)$ is locally connected at x, since Q has property S.

2. Extension of openness

That a mapping may be open on a region R and also open on the boundary of R and yet fail to be open on the closure of R is shown by the mapping of a closed 2-cell A onto the projective plane P by identifying diametrically opposite points on the edge of A. Here the mapping is topological inside A and equivalent to $w = z^2$ on the edge of A but fails to be open on A.

(2.1) THEOREM. *Let X and Y be locally connected generalized continua and let $f(X) = Y$ be a light mapping which is open on $X - f^{-1}(F)$ where F is a closed non-dense set in Y which separates no region in Y and is such that $f^{-1}(F)$ is non-dense. Then f is open on X. (Note: "non-dense" means "contains no open set.")*

Proof. Let $x \, \varepsilon \, f^{-1}(F)$ and let V be any open set in X containing x. We have to show that the point $y = f(x)$ is interior to $f(V)$. Let U be an open set about x such that $\bar{U}$ is compact and contained in V and so that the boundary C of U does not intersect $f^{-1}(y)$. Let R_0 be a region in Y about y so that $\bar{R}_0 \cdot f(C) = \Phi$ and define $R = R_0 - R_0 \cdot F$. Then R is connected and non-empty since F is non-dense. There exists a component G of $f^{-1}(R)$ in U, because $f^{-1}(F)$ is non-dense. This gives $f(G) = R$ by (1.11) since G is conditionally compact, $G \subset X - f^{-1}(F)$ and $f|[X - f^{-1}(F)]$ is open.

Whence, $f(\bar{G}) = \bar{R}$. However, $\bar{R} = \bar{R}_0$ since F is non-dense. Also $\bar{G} \subset U$, because $f(\bar{G}) \cdot f(C) = \Phi$. Accordingly we have

$$f(V) \supset f(U) \supset f(\bar{G}) = \bar{R} \supset R_0$$

so that y is interior to $f(V)$.

(2.11) COROLLARY. *If A and B are closed 2-cells, $\{{}^{or\ n\text{-}cells}_{or\ n\text{-}manifolds}\}$, any light normal mapping of A onto B which is open on the interior of A is open on A.*

Here "normal" means that the interior and edge of A map, respectively, onto the interior and edge of B. The theorem just proven is closely related to the classical theorem that a function of a complex variable which is continuous at an isolated singular point is necessarily analytic there.

3. Open mappings on manifolds

DEFINITION. A separable metric space M is said to be a 2-*dimensional manifold* provided that for any $x \, \varepsilon \, M$ there exists a neighborhood U of x such that $\bar{U}$ is a 2-cell, say $\bar{U} = R + J$ where J is the edge or boundary curve of $\bar{U}$ and R is the interior. If $x \, \varepsilon \, R$, it is an ordinary or regular point of M whereas if $x \, \varepsilon \, J$, it is an edge point (or boundary or singular point) of M. If there are no edge points the manifold is said to be an *ordinary manifold* or a *"closed" manifold*, whereas if there are edge points it is a manifold with boundary.

If β denotes the set of all edge points of a manifold M, since each point of β is a point of order 2 of β and each component of β is open in β while β itself is a closed set, it results that each component of β is either a simple closed curve or an open curve (topological line or open segment). Thus if M is compact, β consists of a finite number (possibly 0) of simple closed curves.

DEFINITION. (Normal mapping and normal region.) If A and B are manifolds or closed regions, a mapping of A on B which maps the edge (or boundary) of A on the edge of B and the interior of A on the interior of B will be said to be a *normal* mapping of A on B. Thus if A and B are manifolds, the edge of A maps on the edge of B and the ordinary part of A maps on the ordinary part of B.

If $f(X) = Y$ is a mapping, a region (or open set) R in X is said to be *normal* (rel. f) provided the set $S = f(R)$ is open in Y and the mapping $f|\bar{R}$ is normal in the sense just defined.

(3.1) *Let X and Y be 2-manifolds where Y is a subset of a plane or a sphere and suppose $f(X) = Y$ is light and open. Let E be any closed 2-cell in X with edge J, let y be any ordinary point of Y in $f(E) - f(J)$ and let $\epsilon > 0$ be given. There exists a circle C in Y with interior R and center y with $\delta(R) < \epsilon$ such that each component of $f^{-1}(\bar{R})$ in E is a closed 2-cell mapping openly and normally onto $\bar{R}$.*

Proof. Since $f^{-1}(y)$ does not separate E, there exists a continuum M in $E - f^{-1}(y)$ which contains $E \cdot f^{-1}f(J)$. There exists a closed circular region N with center y and radius $a < \epsilon$ with $N \subset f(E) - f(M) - Y_e$, where Y_e is the set of all edge points (if any) of Y. By (1.2) there are only a finite number of components $H_1, H_2, \cdots, H_k$ of $f^{-1}(N)$ lying in E. Let $3d = \min. [\rho(H_i, H_j)]$ for $i \neq j$. There exists a $\delta > 0$ with $2\delta < \min. \{\epsilon - a, \rho[N, f(M)]\}$ such that if C is any circle in Y with center y, interior R and radius r with $a < r \leq a + \delta$, then

$$E \cdot f^{-1}(\bar{R}) \subset V_d[E \cdot f^{-1}(N)], \quad \text{and} \quad \bar{R} \subset f(E) - f(M) - Y_e.$$

Now let A be any component of $f^{-1}(\bar{R})$ in E. Since A can contain no point at distance $> d$ from $f^{-1}(N)$, it contains exactly one of the sets H_i and thus just one component Q of $f^{-1}(R)$. Accordingly $A = \bar{Q}$, since every point of A is a limit point of $f^{-1}(R)$ by openness of f. Also $f|A$ is open since A is open in $f^{-1}(\bar{R})$.

Since by (1.4), Q has property S and has no cut point, $\bar{Q}$ is cyclic and locally connected; and hence the boundary K of the component of $X - \bar{Q}$

containing M is a simple closed curve. Now the interior I of K (i.e., the component of $E - K$ lying inside E) contains Q and must be identical with Q, as otherwise it would contain a component of $f^{-1}(Y - \bar{R})$ which would map onto $Y - \bar{R}$; and this is impossible since $I \cdot M = \Phi$ so that $f(I) \cdot f(J) = \Phi$. Accordingly $A = \bar{Q}$ is a closed 2-cell with edge K and interior Q and it maps openly and normally onto $\bar{R}$ under f.

(3.11) COROLLARY. $E \cdot f^{-1}(C)$ consists of a finite number of disjoint simple closed curves each mapping openly onto C.

(3.12) COROLLARY. The same conclusions as in (3.1) and (3.11) hold for any circle C on Y with center y and radius r satisfying $a < r < a + \delta$.

(3.13) COROLLARY. Result (3.1) remains valid without the assumption that Y lies on a plane or sphere if we substitute "simple closed curve C" for "circle C" and "enclosing y" for "center y."

(3.14) COROLLARY. Let X be a 2-manifold and suppose $f(X) = Y$ is light and open. Let E be any closed 2-cell in X with edge J and let $y \; \varepsilon \; f(E) - f(J)$. Then if $\epsilon > 0$ there exists a region R about y in $Y - f(J)$ with $\delta(R) < \epsilon$ and such that each component of $f^{-1}(\bar{R})$ in E is a closed 2-cell mapping openly and normally onto $\bar{R}$.

Since Y is necessarily a locally connected generalized continuum, taking M as in the proof of (1.3) and choosing N as a closed region in $f(E) - f(M)$ having property S, it is clear from that proof that we have only to take R as a sufficiently close region in Y about N so that it has property S.

4. Open mappings on simple cells and manifolds

Two mappings $f(A) = B$ and $\phi(X) = Y$ are said to be *topologically equivalent* provided there exist homeomorphisms $h_1(X) = A$ and $h_2(B) = Y$ satisfying

$$\phi(x) \equiv h_2 f h_1(x)$$

for all $x \; \varepsilon \; X$.

(4.1) If α and β are simple arcs, any normal open mapping of α onto β is topological.

For if some interior point $y \; \varepsilon \; \beta$ had more than one inverse point, there would exist a component Q of $\alpha - f^{-1}(y)$ which contained neither end point of α, whereas by (1.11), $f(Q)$ must contain an end point of β since it is a component of $\beta - y$.

(4.2) Any open mapping $f(J) = C$ of one simple closed curve J on another one C is topologically equivalent to the mapping $w = z^k$ on $|z| = 1$ for some positive integer k.

Proof. Let $a \; \varepsilon \; C$. Since each component of $J - f^{-1}(a)$ maps onto $C - a$, the number of such components and therefore the number of points in $f^{-1}(a)$ must be finite, say k. Then if $b\ \varepsilon\ C - a$, since each component of $J - f^{-1}(a)$ contains a point of $f^{-1}(b)$ and conversely each component of $J - f^{-1}(b)$ contains a point of $f^{-1}(a)$, $f^{-1}(b)$ contains exactly k points and, further, each component of $J - f^{-1}(a)$ maps topologically onto $C - a$. Also these mappings are in the same sense. For let the points of $f^{-1}(a)$ be ordered $a_0, a_1, \cdots, a_{k-1}$ on C in either sense; and let b_i be the point of $f^{-1}(b)$ on $a_j a_{j+1}$ ($a_k = a_0$). Then $a_0 b_0$ maps topologically onto one of the arcs of C from a to b, say axb; $b_0 a_1$ maps topologically onto the other say bya; $a_1 b_1$ maps onto axb; $b_1 a_2$ onto bya; and so on to $b_{k-1} a_0$ which maps topologically onto bya. Clearly this shows that f is topologically equivalent to $w = z^k$ on $|z| = 1$.

For we have only to let h_2 be a homeomorphism of $|w| = 1$ onto C with $h_2(1) = a$, $h_2(i) = x$, $h_2(-1) = b$ and define, for $p\ \varepsilon\ a_j a_{j+1} - a_{j+1}$, ($j = 0, 1, \cdots, k - 1$)

$$h_1(p) = \text{the } (j + 1)\text{st. value of } \sqrt[k]{h_2^{-1} f(p)}$$

$$= \cos \frac{\theta + 2j\pi}{k} + i \sin \frac{\theta + 2j\pi}{k}$$

where $\theta = \text{amp.} [h_2^{-1} f(p)]$.

Note: When the conclusion of (4.2) holds, we shall say that f is of *degree k*.

(4.21) COROLLARY. *Under the conditions of* (3.1) *or* (3.13), $E \cdot f^{-1}(q)$ *is a finite set of points for each* $q\ \varepsilon\ C$.

(4.3) *If* $f(X) = Y$ *is light and open where* X *and* Y *are 2-manifolds and* X *is a closed 2-cell with edge* J, *then for any non-degenerate locally connected continuum* M *in* Y *on which the ordinary points of* $Y - f(J)$ *are dense,* $f^{-1}(M)$ *is locally connected.*

For if y is any ordinary point of Y on $M - f(J)$, any sufficiently small simple closed curve C on Y enclosing y will intersect M. Thus if C is chosen so as to satisfy the conclusion of (3.1) with $E = X$, it follows that $M \cdot C$ contains a point s so that $f^{-1}(s)$ is a finite set and C can be taken arbitrarily small. Thus for the set S of § 1, $S \cdot M$ is dense in M and our conclusion follows from (1.4).

DEFINITIONS. If J is a simple closed curve, a simple arc having just its end points in common with J is said to *span* J. A mapping $g(X) = Y$ is said to be of *multiplicity* $\leq m$ on X provided $g^{-1}(y)$ contains at most m distinct points for any $y\ \varepsilon\ Y$. Also, if t is any arc or single point in Y, we denote by $m(t)$ the number (possibly infinite) of components of $g^{-1}(t)$.

(4.4) *Let* $g(A) = B$ *be light, open and normal, where* A *and* B *are closed 2-cells with edges* C *and* J *respectively. If* $g|C$ *is of degree* k, g *is of multiplicity* $\leq k^2$ *on* A. *Indeed, if* ayb *is any simple arc in* B *spanning* J, *the number of points in* $g^{-1}(y)$ *does not exceed* $m(ay) \cdot m(yb)$.

We shall prove the statement in the last sentence. If this were not so, there would exist components K of $g^{-1}(ay)$ and H of $g^{-1}(yb)$ such that $H \cdot K$ contains at least two points of $g^{-1}(y)$. Now by (4.3), H and K are locally connected continua. Thus since $H \cdot K$ is totally disconnected and contained in $g^{-1}(y)$, it follows that $H + K$ contains a simple closed curve so that there exists a component R of $A - (H + K)$ lying entirely in $A - C$. However, $Fr(R) \subset H + K$; and thus $R \cdot g^{-1}(ayb) = \Phi$, since each component of $g^{-1}(ayb)$ intersects C. Hence $g(R)$ would have to be a component of $B - ayb$; and this is impossible as it does not intersect J.

(4.41) COROLLARY. *If g is topological on C, it is topological on A.*

For in this case $k = 1 = k^2$.

(4.42) COROLLARY. *For any two points y, $z \, \varepsilon \, B$, $m(z) \leqq k \cdot m(y)$. Thus if $m(y) = 1$ for some $y \, \varepsilon \, B$, g is of multiplicity $\leqq k$ on A.*

For, assuming as we may that y, $z \, \varepsilon \, B - J$, there is an arc $azyb$ spanning B; and since $m(zyb) \leqq m(y)$ and $m(az) \leqq k$ our inequality follows directly from (4.4).

(4.5) *Let $g(A) = B$ be a normal light open mapping where A and B are closed 2-cells. If there exists an interior point q of B with a unique inverse point p in A, then on A, g is topologically equivalent to the power mapping $w = z^k$ on $|z| \leqq 1$ for some positive integer k.*

Proof. Let A and B have edges C and J, respectively, and interiors Q and R. Then by (4.2), $g|C$ is topologically equivalent to $w = z^k$ on $|z| \leqq 1$ for some positive integer k. Thus if aqb is an arc in B spanning J, the inverse points a_n and b_n, respectively, of a and b are cyclically ordered $a_0, b_0, a_1, b_1, \cdots, a_{k-1}, b_{k-1}$ on C. Now since each component of $g^{-1}(aqb)$ must contain p, it follows from (4.3) that $g^{-1}(aqb)$ is a locally connected continuum. Thus $g^{-1}(aq)$ contains arcs $a_n p$ and $g^{-1}(bq)$ contains arcs $b_n p$, $n = 0, 1, \cdots, k - 1$. Since for $n \neq j$, $a_n p + a_j p$ separates b_n and b_j in A and does not intersect $(b_n p - p) + (b_j p - p)$, it must separate $b_n p - p$ from $b_j p - p$. Accordingly each pair of the arcs $(b_n p)$ have just p in common and likewise for the arcs $(a_n p)$.

Now let

$$W = \sum_0^{k-1} a_n p + b_n p.$$

Then $W = g^{-1}(aqb)$, because by taking $y = q$ in (4.42) we have that g is of multiplicity $\leqq k$ on A and W already contains k distinct points of $g^{-1}(z)$ for each $z \, \varepsilon \, aqb - q$.

Next we consider the mapping of the simple closed curve $C_n = a_n p + b_n p + a_n b_n$ ($n = 0, 1, \cdots, k - 1$) plus its interior Q_n onto $J_u = aqb + aub$ plus its interior R_u, where $aub = g(a_n b_n)$. If ϕ_n denotes this mapping $g|(C_n + Q_n)$, we have

$$\phi_n(Q_n) = R_u, \quad \phi(C_n) = J_u.$$

Thus ϕ_n is light and normal and $\phi_n|Q_n$ is open. Hence by (2.11), ϕ_n is open on $Q_n + C_n$. Also $\phi_n|C_n$ is topological and thus so also is $\phi_n|(Q_n + C_n)$ by (4.41).

Hence g maps $Q_n + C_n$ topologically onto $J_u + R_u$. Similarly it maps $b_n p + p a_{n+1} + b_n a_{n+1}$ plus its interior topologically onto $aqb + bva$ plus its interior [where $bva = g(b_n a_{n+1})$] and so on alternately. Thus g on A is topologically equivalent to $w = z^k$ on $|z| \leq 1$.

To exhibit this we have only to let h_2 be a homeomorphism of $|w| \leq 1$ onto B with $h_2(0) = q$, $h_2(i) = u$, $h_2(-1, 0) = bq$, $h_2(0, 1) = qa$ and define, for x on $pa_j + a_j a_{j+1} - a_{j+1}$ or within $p a_j a_{j+1} p$ $(j = 0, 1, \cdots, k - 1)$

$$h_1(x) = r^{1/k}\left[\cos\frac{\theta + 2j\pi}{k} + i\sin\frac{\theta + 2j\pi}{k}\right],$$

where $re^{i\theta} = h_2^{-1}g(x)$.

5. Local topological analysis

We are now in position to give a complete local analysis of a light open mapping from X onto Y where X and Y are 2-manifolds without edge points and, indeed, to show that any such mapping is locally equivalent to a power mapping. Thus in case Y is a subset of a complex plane or sphere, a conformal structure can be set up so that X and f constitute a Riemann surface.

(5.1) *Let X and Y be 2-manifolds, where X has no edge points, suppose $f(X) = Y$ is light and open. For any ordinary point $y \varepsilon Y$, $f^{-1}(y)$ is a scattered set.*

For let $x \varepsilon f^{-1}(y)$ and let E be a closed 2-cell on X chosen so that its edge J does not intersect $f^{-1}(y)$. Then by (3.13) there exists a closed 2-cell $\bar{R}$ on X such that each of the finite number of components $A_1, A_2, \cdots A_n$ of $f^{-1}(\bar{R})$ lying in E maps openly and normally onto $\bar{R}$. Then by (4.4) it follows that the total number of points of $E \cdot f^{-1}(y)$ cannot exceed the sum of the squares of the degrees of the mappings of the edges of A_j onto the edge of $\bar{R}$ and each of these degrees is finite by (4.2). Hence $f^{-1}(y)$ is scattered.

(5.2) THEOREM. *Let $f(X) = Y$ be light and open where X and Y are 2-manifolds and X is without boundary, let q be any ordinary point of Y and let $p \varepsilon f^{-1}(q)$. There exists an integer $k > 0$ such that if B is any sufficiently small closed 2-cell on Y with q in its interior, the component A of $f^{-1}(B)$ containing p is a closed 2-cell mapping onto B by a power map of degree k, i.e., $f|A$ is topologically equivalent to $w = z^k$ on $|z| \leq 1$.*

Proof. Let E be a closed 2-cell on X about p with edge J such that $E \cdot f^{-1}(q) = p$. By (3.13) there exists a closed 2-cell B' about q lying in $Y - f(J)$ such that the component A' of $f^{-1}(B')$ containing p is a closed

2-cell and maps openly and normally onto B'; and since $A' \subset E$ so that $A' \cdot f^{-1}(q) = p$, it follows from (4.5) that $f|A'$ is topologically equivalent to $w = z^k$ on $|z| \leq 1$ for some $k > 0$. Now it is clear that our conclusion holds for this k and for any closed 2-cell B about p satisfying $B \subset B'$, thus in particular for any B with $\delta(B) < \rho(q,$ edge of $B')$.

Clearly (4.5) together with the method of proof used for (3.1) will give

(5.21) COROLLARY. *Let X, Y, f, p and q be as above. Let E be any closed 2-cell about p on X with edge J, $p = E \cdot f^{-1}(q)$, and $f(E) \neq Y$. Then there exists an integer $k > 0$ such that if B is any closed 2-cell about q with $B \subset Y - f(J)$, the component A of $f^{-1}(B)$ containing p is a closed 2-cell mapping onto B by a power map of degree k.*

If in addition Y is an open subset of a plane or sphere, the conclusions of (5.2) hold for any sufficiently small circular disk with center q where q is any point whatever of Y. Thus we have

(5.3) THEOREM. *Let $f(X) = Y$ be light and open where X is a 2-manifold without boundary and Y is an open subset of a plane or sphere. Then there exists a conformal structure on X given by f so that (X, f) becomes a Riemann surface.*

This means X is representable as a finite or countable union of closed 2-cells.

$$X = \sum A_n$$

each of which intersects only finitely many of the others and each of which maps under f onto a closed circular region in Y by a mapping topologically equivalent to a power mapping $w = z^k$ on $|z| \leq 1$ for some positive integer k.

In concluding this section we note that in results (5.1) and (5.2) the restriction that X have no edge points can now be dropped. All that was essential for the proofs of these results was that the point y or q be an ordinary point of Y which is not the image of an edge point of X. It is now easily shown that an ordinary point of Y can never be the image of an edge point of X; that is,

(5.4) *Let $f(X) = Y$ be light and open where X and Y are 2-manifolds. If p is an edge point of X, its image $q = f(p)$ is an edge point of Y.*

For suppose q is an ordinary point of Y. Let p have a closed 2-cell neighborhood A with edge consisting of an arc apb of the edge of X together with an arc aub so that $aub - (a + b)$ consists of ordinary points of X. Let h be a homeomorphism of the lower half $(y \leq 0)$ of the unit disk $|z| \leq 1$ of the z-plane onto A so that $h(-1) = a$, $h(0) = p$, $h(1) = b$. Let X' be the open disk $|z| < 1$ and define a mapping g of X' into Y as follows:

$$g(z) = fh(z) \quad \text{for} \quad y \leq 0 \quad \text{where} \quad z = x + iy$$
$$g(z) = fh(\bar{z}) \quad \text{for} \quad y > 0 \quad \text{where} \quad \bar{z} = x - iy$$

Then clearly g is light and open on X'; and since $Y' = g(X') = f(A - aub)$, q is an ordinary point of Y'. Hence by (5.3) g would be equivalent to a power mapping on some disk neighborhood of p. This is impossible since g fails to be locally topological at all points of the real axis.

Our conclusions in (5.2) may now be summarized and slightly extended in the following statement:

(5.5) THEOREM. *Let* $f(X) = Y$ *be light and open where* X *and* Y *are* 2-*manifolds. If* q *is any ordinary point in* Y *and if we take any finite sequence of points* $p_1, p_2, \cdots, p_n$ *of* $f^{-1}(q)$, *then for any sufficiently small closed* 2-*cell neighborhood* W *of* q *in* Y, *the components* $E_1, E_2, \cdots, E_n$ *of* $f^{-1}(W)$ *containing* $p_1, p_2, \cdots, p_n$ *respectively are disjoint and each is a closed* 2-*cell which maps onto* W *by a power map, i.e., a mapping topologically equivalent to* $w = z^k$ *on* $|z| \leq 1$ *for some* $k > 0$.

6. Degree. Compact mappings

We recall that a mapping f of A into B is *compact* provided that for every compact set K in B, $f^{-1}(K)$ is compact or, equivalently, that f is closed and the inverse of each point of B is compact. If k is a positive integer, a mapping $f(A) = B$ is said to be of *degree* k provided that for each $q \, \varepsilon \, B$ the sum of the multiplicities of the points in $f^{-1}(q)$ is k, where $p_i \, \varepsilon f^{-1}(q)$ has multiplicity k_i provided that on a 2-cell neighborhood of p_i, f is topologically equivalent to $w = z^{k_i}$ on $|z| \leq 1$.

(6.1) THEOREM. *If* A *and* B *are* 2-*manifolds without edges* (B *connected,* A *not necessarily connected), a light open mapping* $f(A) = B$ *has a finite degree if and only if it is compact.*

Proof. Suppose f is compact. Then by (5.5) it follows that for each $y \, \varepsilon \, B$ there exists a neighborhood W of y and an integer $k(y)$ such that every point p in $W - y$ has exactly $k(y)$ inverse points. Indeed $k(y)$ is merely the local degree at y or the sum of the multiplicities at the points of $f^{-1}(y)$, i.e., the sum of the integers k_i, $i = 1, 2, \cdots, n$, where f is topologically equivalent to $w = z^{k_i}$, $|z| \leq 1$ on the set E_i. If we consider $k(y)$ as a function on B, it is therefore continuous and thus must be constant, say $k(y) = k$, on B as B is connected. Thus f is of degree k.

On the other hand suppose f is of degree k. Let K be any compact set in B. By (5.5) each $q \, \varepsilon \, K$ is interior to a set W such that there are disjoint components $E_1, E_2, \cdots, E_n$ of $f^{-1}(W)$ containing $p_1, \cdots, p_n$ respectively where $f^{-1}(q) = p_1 + p_2 + \cdots + p_n$ and such that the E_i map onto W by power mappings of degree k_i with $\sum_{i=1}^{n} k_i = k$. Since each point of $W - q$ then has k distinct inverse points in $\sum_{1}^{n} E_i$, it follows that $f^{-1}(W) = \sum_{1}^{n} E_i$ and thus that $f^{-1}(W)$ is compact. Since K is covered by a finite number of such sets W, it follows that $f^{-1}(K)$ is compact.

(6.11) COROLLARY. *If $f(A) = B$ is a light open mapping of degree k, the points $y \, \varepsilon \, B$ having less than k distinct inverses form a completely scattered set D. On the set $A - f^{-1}(D)$, f is a local homeomorphism.*

(6.2) THEOREM. *Let A and B be separable metric spaces, let f be any mapping of A into B and let R be any set in B. For any non-empty conditionally compact component Q of $f^{-1}(R)$ or any conditionally compact set in $f^{-1}(R)$ which is closed relative to $f^{-1}(R)$, the mapping of Q into R by f is a compact mapping.*

Proof. Denote $f|Q$ by g and let K be any compact set in R. Then since $f^{-1}(K)$ is closed and $\bar{Q}$ is compact, $\bar{Q} \cdot f^{-1}(K)$ is compact. But $\bar{Q} \cdot f^{-1}(K) = Q \cdot f^{-1}(K) = g^{-1}(K)$ since $(\bar{Q} - Q) \cdot f^{-1}(K) \subset (\bar{Q} - Q) \cdot f^{-1}(R) = \Phi$.

(6.21) COROLLARY. *If A and B are locally connected generalized continua, f is open on $f^{-1}(R)$ where R is a region in B, and Q is a conditionally compact component of $f^{-1}(R)$, then $f(Q) = R$ and $f|Q : Q \to R$ is compact.*

For since Q is open in A, $f(Q)$ is both open and closed in R and thus is equal to R.

IX. Global Analysis

1. The Stoïlow Theorem

We are now in position to establish this fundamental result to the effect that any light open mapping from a 2-manifold without boundary to the complex plane is topologically equivalent to an analytic function. More precisely,

(1.1) THEOREM. *Let* $I(X) = Y$ *be light and open where* X *is a 2-manifold without boundary and* Y *is a region in a complex plane* W. *Then there exists an analytic function* $w = \phi(z)$, *single valued on its Riemann surface* R, *and a homeomorphism* $T(R) = X$ *such that*

$$IT(q) \equiv \phi(q) \qquad \text{for all } q \, \varepsilon \, R.$$

By VIII, (5.3) there exists a conformal structure on X given by I so that (X, I) becomes a Riemann surface R'. By the well known Riemann-Koebe theorem there exists an analytic function

$$(1) \qquad z = f(w) \qquad \text{(in general multiple valued)}$$

which has $R' = (X, I)$ as its Riemann surface. This means that for each $w \, \varepsilon \, Y$ we have positions $(x_1, I), (x_2, I), \cdots$ on R' corresponding strictly (1-1) to the points $x_1, x_2, \cdots$ of $I^{-1}(w)$ and likewise to the distinct values $z_1 = f(x_1, I), z_2 = f(x_2, I), \cdots$ of $f(w)$. Thus if

$$(2) \qquad w = \phi(z)$$

is the inverse function to (1), ϕ is analytic and is single valued on its Riemann surface R. Indeed we have $\phi(z_j) = f^{-1}(z_j) = I(x_j, I) = w$ for $j = 1, 2, \cdots$.

We next define a homeomorphism $T(R) = X$. Let π be the projecting function for R, i.e., for $q \, \varepsilon \, R$, $\pi(q)$ is the value z_q of z over which the position q on R is located, so that q is one of the positions created in R corresponding to one of possibly many values of $\phi(z)$ at z_q. Now for $q \, \varepsilon \, R$ we define $p = T(q)$ as the unique point of $I^{-1}\phi(q)$ which maps onto $z_q = \pi(q)$ under f, that is

$$(3) \qquad T(q) = [I^{-1}\phi(q)] \cdot [f^{-1}\pi(q)]$$

Then T is single valued and we have at once

(4) $T^{-1}(p) = [\phi^{-1}I(p)] \cdot [\pi^{-1}f(p)]$,   for all $p \ \varepsilon \ X$,

i.e., $q = T^{-1}(p)$ is the unique point of $\pi^{-1}f(p)$ which maps onto $w = I(p)$ under ϕ.

Now if U and V are open sets in X and R, respectively, the sets

$$T(V) = [I^{-1}\phi(V)] \cdot [f^{-1}\pi(V)]$$

$$T^{-1}(U) = [\phi^{-1}I(U)] \cdot [\pi^{-1}f(U)]$$

given by (3) and (4) are open by continuity and openness of the mappings f, ϕ, I and π. Hence both T and T^{-1} are single valued and open so that T is a homeomorphism; and by the definition (3) we have

$$IT(q) \equiv \phi(q), \qquad q \ \varepsilon \ R$$

2. Orientability.

By a (straight) 0-, 1- or 2-dimensional *simplex* is meant a point, line segment, or triangle plus its interior respectively. The end points of a 1-simplex are called its vertices or *0-sides*. The sides of a triangle are the 1-sides of the 2-simplex defined by the triangle and the vertices of the triangle are its 0-sides or simply its vertices. A set homeomorphic with a simplex is called a *curved simplex*, with dimensionality and sides determined in obvious manner from the homeomorphism. A *complex* is a set K of simplexes (straight or curved) such that (1) any side of a simplex of K is itself a simplex of K, (2) the intersection of any two simplexes of K is either empty or a side of both simplexes and (3) any point on a simplex of K has a neighborhood which intersects only a finite number of simplexes of K. A *simplicial subdivision* of a set M is a representation of M as the union of a set of simplexes (straight or curved) which form a complex in the sense just defined. In our considerations, the set M will be a 2-dimensional manifold. If K is a finite 2-dimensional complex (i.e., has only a finite number of simplexes), the *Euler characteristic* $\chi(K)$ is the number $\alpha_0 - \alpha_1 + \alpha_2$, where α_j is the number of j-simplexes in K, $j = 0$, 1, 2. If M is a compact set, any simplicial subdivision of M is a finite complex K and we set $\chi(M) = \chi(K)$. It can be verified that $\chi(M)$ is independent of the particular subdivision K used.

An orientation of a straight or curved triangle Δ with vertices a, b, and c is determined by an ordering of its vertices. For example (a, b, c) and (b, a, c) determine (opposite) orientations of Δ. Now an orientation (a, b, c) of a triangle Δ, straight or curved, induces orientations (a, b), (b, c), (c, a) onto the sides or segments of the sides of Δ. Two orientations of the same triangle are the same provided the orderings of vertices in one can be changed to the ordering in the other by an even number of interchanges. Thus (a, b, c) and (b, c, a) are the same whereas (b, a, c) and (a, b, c) are opposite. Thus each triangle, or 2-cell, Δ has exactly two distinct orientations and these correspond precisely to the two senses of traversals of its boundary. A traversal of the boundary of Δ determines a sense a, b, c of permutation of the vertices of Δ and thus corresponds uniquely to an orientation of Δ and conversely. Two oriented triangles or 2-cells lying together in a plane or on a 2-cell are said to *agree in orientation* provided the corresponding traversals of their boundaries agree in sense as defined in Chapter V, § 2. Thus as shown there, if a 2-cell A' with edge J' lies interior to a 2-cell A with edge J and a, b, c and a', b', c' are triples of distinct points on J and J' respectively, the orientations (a, b, c) of A and (a', b', c') of A' as simplexes will agree if and only if there exist disjoint simple arcs aa', bb', cc' lying except for their ends in the annular region of A between J and J'. Also if two oriented triangles or 2-cells (a, b, c) and (x, y, z) otherwise disjoint and lying in a plane or a 2-cell are so situated that a side xy of (x, y, z) lies in a side ab of (a, b, c) and the corresponding traversals abc and xyz of their boundaries agree in sense on xy, then the orientations (a, b, c) and (x, y, z) will be the same or opposite according as Δxyz lies except for xy entirely inside or entirely outside Δabc.

A 2-dimensional manifold M is said to be *orientable* provided orientations can be so assigned to the curved triangles in a *triangulation* of M, i.e., a simplicial subdivision of M, that any pair of triangles with a common side will be "coherently" oriented in that the common side obtains opposite induced orientations from the two triangles. If such an assignment of orientations is not possible, M is said to be non-orientable. It is readily seen that if M is orientable it has exactly two different orientations and these are said to be opposite. It is true, though not obvious, that the property of being orientable is independent of any particular triangulation of M and in fact dependent only on the topological structure of M itself. If one triangulation of M can be oriented, then so can any other triangulation of M. This in particular is a direct consequence of the main theorem of this section now to be established.

(2.1) THEOREM. *Let* $f(A) = B$ *be light, open and normal, where* A *and* B *are 2-manifolds. Then if* B *is orientable, so also is* A.

Proof. Let T_a and T_b be triangulations of A and B respectively and let T_b be oriented. For each triangle Δ in T_a we assign an orientation as follows. Let δ be a triangle interior to Δ which does not intersect the set W of all points x of A such that f fails to be locally topological at some point of $f^{-1}f(x)$ together with all edge points of A and which is small enough that δ maps topologically onto its image γ under f and so that γ lies inside a triangle Γ of T_b Then if a, b, and c are the vertices of δ, we give δ such an orientation (a, b, c) that $[f(a), f(b), f(c)]$ is the positive orientation of γ in B, i.e., this orientation in γ agrees with the given orientation of Γ in T_b. We then assign an orientation to Δ so as to agree with that just given to δ. Thus we assign an orientation to each triangle Δ in T_a. Now to show that this yields an admissible orientation of A, we must show that any pair of triangles Δ_1 and Δ_2 in T_a with a common side ab are coherently oriented in the sense that the induced orientations of ab from the orienta- tions of the two triangles Δ_1 and Δ_2 are opposite. To this end let δ_1 and δ_2 be the triangles in Δ_1 and Δ_2 respectively which determine the orienta- tions as defined above. Since $A - W$ is connected and open and contains δ_1 and δ_2, it contains a chain of triangles.

$$\delta_1 = \sigma_1, \sigma_2, \cdots, \sigma_k, \sigma_{k+1}, \cdots, \sigma_n = \delta_2$$

such that (1) σ_i and σ_{i+1} intersect in a common side for $i = 1, 2, \cdots$, $n - 1$, and $\sigma_i \cdot \sigma_j$ is at most a common vertex for $j > i + 1$, (2) $\sigma_i \subset \Delta_1$ for $i \leq k$ and $\sigma_i \subset \Delta_2$ for $i > k$ so that the common side $\alpha\beta$ of σ_k and σ_{k+1} lies in ab, and (3) so that f is topological on the union of any pair $\sigma_i + \sigma_{i+1}$ of successive triangles in the chain and $f(\sigma_i + \sigma_{i+1})$ intersects at most one edge (i.e., 1-simplex, of T_b and thus lies interior either to a single triangle of T_b or to the union of two triangles of T_b. To obtain the chain so as to satisfy (3) we note that there are only a finite set F of points interior to $\Delta_1 + \Delta_2$ which either belong to W or map into a vertex of T_b. Then if we take simple arcs $a_1 p$ and $p a_2$ in $\Delta_1 - F$ and $\Delta_2 - F$ respectively with $p \varepsilon ab$ and $a_1 p - p$ interior to Δ_1, $a_2 p - p$ interior to Δ_2, any chain in $\Delta_1 + \Delta_2$ satisfying (1) and (2) and of *sufficiently small mesh* will neces- sarily satisfy (3) provided each link of the chain intersects $t = a_1 p + p a_2$, because f is locally topological at all points of t and $f(t)$ contains no vertex of T_b. Thus we have only to construct the chain using the arc t as a guide with each link intersecting t and being of sufficiently small diameter.

Now for each i, $f(\sigma_i)$ lies interior to a 2-cell E which is either a single triangle of T_b or the union of two such triangles with a side in common. Thus in either case E is oriented by the given orientation of T_b. Now if for each i we assign such an orientation (a_i, b_i, c_i) in σ_i that $[f(a_i), f(b_i), f(c_i)]$ agrees in E with the given orientation in T_b, it follows by property (3) that any two successive triangles σ_i and σ_{i+1} in the chain are coherently oriented because $f(\sigma_i + \sigma_{i+1})$ is a 2-cell interior to such a cell E on B with which both $f(\sigma_i)$ and $f(\sigma_{i+1})$ agree in orientation. Thus σ_i for $i \leq k$ has the same orientation as does $\sigma_1 = \delta_1$ and hence the same as Δ_1, and σ_i for $i > k$ agrees in orientation with $\sigma_n = \delta_2$ and thus with Δ_2. Since $\alpha\beta$ therefore receives opposite induced orientations from σ_k and σ_{k+1}, the common side ab of Δ_1 and Δ_2 which contains $\alpha\beta$ likewise receives opposite induced orientations from Δ_1 and Δ_2. Accordingly Δ_1 and Δ_2 are coherently oriented.

(2.11) *Non-orientability is invariant under light open mappings of ordinary 2-manifolds onto ordinary 2-manifolds.*.

Note: This is not valid for manifolds with edges. For a projective plane can be mapped onto a 2-cell by a light open mapping, although of course the mapping cannot be normal.

Also it is not true that orientability is invariant under light open mappings on ordinary manifolds. For the sphere maps readily onto a projective plane by 2-1 local homeomorphism.

(2.12) *Orientability is a topological invariant for 2-manifolds. If one triangulation of a given 2-manifold admits an orientation, so also does any other.*

To get the first statement we have only to apply the above theorem to h^{-1}, where $h(A) = B$ is a homeomorphism. For the second, we let h be the identity and work with T_a and T_b as in the above proof.

We next prove a sort of converse

(2.2) THEOREM. *Every orientable (connected separable and thus tri-angulable) 2-manifold without boundary admits a light open mapping onto the 2-sphere S^2.*

Proof. We consider a triangulation T of the given surface X and first effect a "barycentric" or "central" subdivision of each triangle Δ of T. That is, the vertices a and the "midpoints" b of the three sides of Δ are joined to a chosen interior point c of Δ so as to divide Δ into six triangles. Since the surface X is orientable, it is possible to assign unambiguously to each of the 2-cells of the barycentric subdivision of the given triangulation one of the designations "shaded," "unshaded" in such a manner that no two distinct 2-cells of the same designation have an edge in common. This may be achieved as follows. Each 2-cell of the subdivision has precisely one edge which lies on a 1-cell of the original triangulation. If this edge contains the "initial" point of the 1-cell where "initial" is taken in the sense of the orientation of the 2-cell of the original triangulation which contains the given 2-cell of the subdivision, we term the 2-cell of the subdivision "shaded," otherwise "unshaded."

We let α, β, γ denote three distinct points of the equator of S^2, $\alpha\beta$ the arc free from γ, and so on, and map the 1-cells ab homeomorphically onto $\alpha\beta$ so that a goes into α and b into β, and proceed similarly for the 1-cells bc and ca onto $\beta\gamma$ and $\gamma\alpha$ respectively. On each "shaded" 2-cell the mapping can be extended to a homeomorphic mapping of the 2-cell onto the closed northern hemisphere and similarly on each "unshaded" 2-cell the mapping can be extended to a homeomorphic mapping of the 2-cell onto the closed southern hemisphere. The resulting map of the surface onto S^2 fulfills all the imposed conditions. Then as a consequence of these two results, along with the theorem in § 1, we have

(2.3) THEOREM. *A (connected separable) 2-manifold without boundary is a Riemann surface if and only if it is orientable.*

3. Characteristic equation for compact manifolds.

We begin with a characterization of normality.

(3.1) THEOREM. *If X and Y are 2-manifolds with edges α and β, a light open mapping $f(X) = Y$ is normal if and only if it is locally topological at all points of $f^{-1}(\beta)$.*

Proof. Suppose this condition holds. Then since $f(\alpha) \subset \beta$ in any case, to show normality of f we have only to verify that $f^{-1}(\beta) \subset \alpha$. This is an obvious consequence of our condition, since any ordinary point of X where f is locally topological must map onto an ordinary point of Y.

Now suppose f is normal. We then must show that f is locally topological at each point x of α. To this end we first show that the mapping $f|\alpha$, i.e., $f(\alpha) = \beta$, is locally topological at x. Let $y = f(x)$ and let pyq be an arc in the component D of β containing y. Then take an arc axb in α so that $f(axb) \subset pyq - p - q$. Then $f|axb$ must be topological. For if $x_1, x_2 \varepsilon axb$, $x_1 \neq x_2$ and $f(x_1) = f(x_2) = z$, then the arc x_1x_2 of axb would contain a component of $f^{-1}(D - z)$ and hence would map onto a set containing a component of $D - y$ and thus containing either p or q, and this is impossible since $f(axb) \subset pyq - p - q$.

Now let E and G be disks in X and Y respectively with edges $axbua$ and $pyqvp$ respectively, where $f(E) \subset G$, $axb \subset \alpha$, $pyq \subset \beta$ and f maps axb topologically onto a subarc p_1yq_1 of pyq with $f(a) = p_1$, $f(x) = y$. Let h be a homeomorphism mapping the lower half of the disk $|z| \leq 1$ of the z-plane onto E with $h(-1) = a$, $h(0) = x$, $h(1) = b$; and let s be a homeomorphism mapping the disk G onto the lower half of the disk $|w| \leq 1$ of the w-plane with $s(p) = -1$, $s(y) = 0$, $s(q) = 1$.

Next let X' be the manifold $|z| < 1$ and define a mapping g of X' into $|w| < 1$ as follows

$$w = g(z) = sfh(z) \quad \text{for} \quad \xi \leq 0 \quad \text{where } z = \zeta + i\xi$$

$$w = g(z) = \overline{sfh(\bar{z})} \quad \text{for} \quad \xi > 0 \quad \text{(where the bar denotes the complex conjugate).}$$

Clearly this mapping is light and open; also since $g(X')$ contains a neighborhood of the origin $0 = s(y)$ in the w-plane, 0 is an ordinary point of $g(X')$. Hence by (5.5) g maps some disk neighborhood of $z = 0$ onto a similar neighborhood of $w = 0$ by a power mapping of degree k. However, since $f|axb$ is topological, $k = 1$. Thus f is locally topological at x.

(3.11) COROLLARY. *If f is normal, it is locally topological at all edge points of X.*

For a light open mapping $f(A) = B$, A and B 2-manifolds, a point $y \varepsilon B$ is a *singular point* if f fails to be locally topological at some point of $f^{-1}(y)$.

(3.2) THEOREM. *Let A and B be compact 2-manifolds and let $f(A) = B$ be light, open and normal. Then*

$$k\chi(B) - \chi(A) = kr - n,$$

where k is the degree of f, r is the number of singular points of f on B and n is the number of inverse points in A of these r singular points.

Proof. Let α and β be the edges of A and B respectively. Then f must be locally topological at all points of α.

Now let $Q = q_1 + q_2 + \cdots + q_r$ be all the singular points of f on B, i.e., the points (if any) of B having at least one inverse point at which f is not locally topological. By what was just shown it follows that r and n are finite. For each $i \leq r$, let $f^{-1}(q_i) = p_{i1} + p_{i2} + \cdots + p_{in_i}$. By VIII, § 5, there exist disjoint closed 2-cell neighborhoods $W_1, W_2, \cdots, W_r$ of $q_1, \cdots, q_r$ respectively so that for each $i \leq r$, $f^{-1}(W_i)$ consists of n_i disjoint 2-cells $W_{i1}, W_{i2}, \cdots, W_{in_i}$ so that W_{ij} contains p_{ij} in its interior and maps onto W_i by a power mapping. For each $i \leq r$, let S_i be a simple arc in W_i containing q_i and having just its end points on the edge of W_i. Let $T_{ij} = W_{ij} \cdot f^{-1}(S_i), j = 1, \cdots, n_i$ and let $T = \sum \sum T_{ij}$.

There exists a number $e > 0$ such that for any connected set E in $A - T$ of diameter $< e$, f is topological on $\bar{E}$. For if not, there would exist a sequence $E_1, E_2, \cdots$ of connected sets with $\delta(E_n) \rightarrow 0$ and which converges to a point p of A and such that for each n some two points of E_n have the same image under f. Since f is locally topological on $A - f^{-1}(Q)$, we must have $p = p_{ij}$ for some i and j. But then for n sufficiently large, E_n lies interior to W_{ij} and does not intersect T_{ij}, whereas f is topological on the closure of each component of $W_{ij} - T_{ji}$.

Next, since f is light, there exists a $d > 0$ such that for any set N in B of diameter $< d$, each component $f^{-1}(N)$ is of diameter $< e$. Now let H be any simplicial subdivision of B of norm $< d$ such that each S_i, $i = 1, 2, \cdots, r$, is included in the one dimensional structure of H. Then if Δ_0 is the interior of any 2-simplex Δ of H, the components of $f^{-1}(\Delta_0)$ are of diameter $< e$; and as they lie in $A - T$, the closure of each is a 2-cell mapping topologically onto Δ. Thus if for each such Δ and component G of $f^{-1}(\Delta_0)$ we select sides and vertices of $\bar{G}$ as images of corresponding sides and vertices under the topological mapping $f^{-1} \colon \Delta \rightarrow \bar{G}$, we obtain a simplicial subdivision of A into a complex K such that each simplex of K maps topologically onto a simplex of H under f.

Let α_m and β_m $(m = 0, 1, 2)$ be the number of m-simplexes in K and H respectively and let $n = \sum n_i = $ the total number of points in $f^{-1}(Q)$. Then since f is of degree k and is locally topological on $A - f^{-1}(Q)$, we have

$$\alpha_2 = k\beta_2$$

$$\alpha_1 = k\beta_1$$

$$\alpha_0 = k(\beta_0 - r) + n.$$

Whence,

$$\alpha_2 - \alpha_1 + \alpha_0 = k(\beta_2 - \beta_1 + \beta_0) - kr + n.$$

or $k\chi(B) - \chi(A) = kr - n$.

Remark. Given a local homeomorphism $f(X) = Y$. If C is any simple closed curve in Y, every component of $f^{-1}(C)$ is either a simple closed curve or an open curve (topological line). This results at once from the fact that these two types of sets are the only ones locally homeomorphic with an open segment. This leads at once to the following:

(3.3) *If A_0 and B_0 are 2-manifolds without edges and $f(A_0) = B_0$ is light and open and B is any 2-manifold on B_0 whose edge contains no singular point of f, then any compact component A of $f^{-1}(B)$ is a 2-manifold which maps normally, lightly and openly onto B and the relation $k\chi(B) - \chi(A) = kr - n$ holds.*

Proof. For if Q is a component of $f^{-1}(R)$ in A, where R is the ordinary part of B, then Q is bounded by a finite number of simple closed curves in $f^{-1}(\beta)$, where β is the edge of B. Thus $\bar{Q}$ is a manifold; and $\bar{Q}$ must be equal to A because each edge point of Q is on the boundary of a region of $A_0 - \bar{Q}$ which maps into $B_0 - B$, so that there can be no other component of $f^{-1}(R)$ in A except Q.

Appendix

Topological Background for the Maximum Principle

1. Exponential representations. Indices.

We take an arbitrary mapping $\phi(x)$ of an interval or simple arc ab into the complex plane Z and let p be a point of $Z - E$, where $E = \phi(ab)$ is the image of ab. Any continuous function $u(x)$, $x \varepsilon ab$, satisfying

$$(1) \qquad\qquad e^{u(x)} = \phi(x) - p, \qquad x \varepsilon ab,$$

is called a *continuous branch* of the logarithm of $\phi(x) - p$ and (1) is referred to as an *exponential representation* of $\phi(x) - p$.

It is readily shown that: *Every ϕ has such a representation and, further, the $u(x)$ is uniquely determined up to an additive constant.* For let $a = x_0, x_1, \cdots, x_n = b$ be a subdivision of ab so that $\phi(x_j x_{j+1})$ lies inside a circle not enclosing p for each $j = 0, 1, \cdots, n - 1$. Then for any j there is a ray pq_j from p not intersecting $\phi(x_j x_{j+1})$; and if $u(x_j) = \log |\phi(x_j) - p| + i\theta_j$ is any preassigned value of $\log [\phi(x_j) - p]$, we have only to define

$$u(x) = \log |\phi(x) - p| + i(\theta_j + \theta_x), \qquad x \varepsilon x_j x_{j+1},$$

where θ_x is the signed angle, $-2\pi < \theta_x < 2\pi$, from the ray $p\phi(x_j)$ to the ray $p\phi(x)$ not containing the ray pq_j, to obtain a representation (1) of $\phi(x) - p$ on $x_j x_{j+1}$. Thus if we take such a representation on $x_0 x_1$ given by $u(x)$, it can be extended to $x_1 x_2$ with agreement at x_1, thence to $x_2 x_3$ with agreement at x_2 and so on to x_n. To see that this representation is unique up to an additive constant, we have only to note that $e^{u(x)} = e^{v(x)}$ on a connected set I implies $u(x) - v(x) = 2k\pi i$ on I for some fixed integer k, because $u(x) - v(x)$ is continuous on I and is always a value of $\log 1$.

Thus when we define the *circulation index*

$$(2) \qquad\qquad \mu_{ab}(\phi, p) = u(b) - u(a)$$

of ϕ about p it follows that μ is independent of the particular $u(x)$ entering into the representation (1). Also, of course,

(3) $\mu(\phi, p) = \mu(\phi - p, 0)$

and for any factorization $\phi(x) - p = \phi_1(x) \cdot \phi_2(x)$, we have

(4) $\mu(\phi, p) = \mu(\phi_1, 0) + \mu(\phi_2, 0)$.

We note here that when confusion is unlikely to result, some or all of the symbols ab, ϕ, and p in the expression $\mu_{ab}(\phi, p)$ may and will be omitted.

Now in case $\phi(b) = \phi(a)$ so that our "curve" or image is closed, $\mu(\phi, p)$ has the form $2k\pi i$, k an integer, so that $\mu(\phi, p)/2\pi i = w(\phi, p)$ is integer valued and is called the *winding number* of ϕ about p. For $u(x)$ is a logarithm of $\phi(x) - p$ and thus is of the form $\log |\phi(x) - p| + i$ amp $[\phi(x) - p]$.

(1.1) *As a function of p, $\mu(\phi, p)$ is continuous in p and thus is constant in each component of $Z - E$.*

For if $g(x) = (p - p_1)/[\phi(x) - p]$, $x \, \varepsilon \, ab$, we have

$$\phi(x) - p_1 = (\phi(x) - p)[g(x) - (-1)]$$

so that $\mu(\phi, p_1) = \mu(\phi, p) + \mu(g, -1)$. Thus if p_1 is any point inside a circle with center p and radius $\rho(p, E)$, $g(ab)$ lies within the circle $|z| = 1$; and $\mu(g, -1)$ will be 0 since the variation of the imaginary part of the $u(x)$ in a representation of $g(x) - (-1)$ would be $< 2\pi$ in modulus since $g(ab)$ cannot intersect the negative real axis between -1 and ∞.

From this follows

(1.2) $\mu(\phi, p) = 0$ *for all points p in the unbounded component of $Z - E$.*

Indeed, for some such p sufficiently remote from E, the angle subtended by E at p is $< 2\pi$. Hence again the variation of the imaginary part of $u(x)$ is $< 2\pi$ in modulus so that $k = 0$ and $\mu = 0$.

(1.3) *For any sense preserving homeomorphism $h(ab) = \alpha\beta$, [i.e., $h(a) = \alpha$], we have*

$$\mu_{ab}(\phi, p) = u_{\alpha\beta}(\phi h^{-1}, p).$$

For if $\phi_1(x) = \phi h^{-1}(x)$ and $u_1(x) = uh^{-1}(x)$, $x \, \varepsilon \, \alpha\beta$, where $e^{u(x)} = \phi(x) - p$, $x \, \varepsilon \, ab$, we have

$$e^{u_1(x)} = e^{uh^{-1}(x)} = \phi h^{-1}(x) - p = \phi_1(x) - p, \, x \, \varepsilon \, \alpha\beta,$$

and

$$u_1(\beta) - u_1(\alpha) = uh^{-1}(\beta) - uh^{-1}(\alpha) = u(b) - u(a).$$

2. Traversals.

Now let C be a simple closed curve and let f be a continuous function from C to the complex plane Z. We understand by a *traversal* of C a mapping ζ of an interval or simple arc ab onto C with $\zeta(a) = \zeta(b)$ but with $\zeta^{-1}(y)$ unique for $y \,\varepsilon\, C - \zeta(a)$. It is readily shown that $\mu_{ab}(f\,\zeta, p)$ depends only on the *sense* in which ζ traverses C, i.e., if α, β, γ are distinct points on C, on whether, as x moves from a to b on ab, $\zeta(x)$ takes on an even or an odd permutation of the order α, β, γ of these values. For we have

(2.1) *For any two sense agreeing traversals ζ and ζ_1 of C,*

$$\mu(f\zeta, p) = \mu(f\zeta_1, p).$$

To show this, let $\phi = f\zeta$, $\phi_1 = f\zeta_1$. Then if ζ_1 maps $a_1 b_1$ onto J, clearly we may suppose $\zeta(a) = \zeta_1(a_1)$; and $h(x) = \zeta_1^{-1}\,\zeta(x)$ for $x \neq a$, b, $h(a) = a_1$, $h(b) = b_1$ is a sense preserving homeomorphism of ab onto $a_1 b_1$. Whence $\phi h^{-1} = f\zeta\zeta^{-1}\zeta_1 = f\zeta_1 = \phi_1$ and our conclusion now follows by (1.3).

Now in case C is a circle in Z with center p and radius r, by taking f to be the identity mapping $f(z) = z$ it follows by (2.1) that any traversal of C agreeing in sense with that defined by

$$\zeta(x) - p = e^{2\pi i x + \log r}, \ 0 \leq x \leq 1, \ x \text{ real},$$

has index $\mu(\zeta, p) = 2\pi i$ and all other traversals of C have index $-2\pi i$ since they agree in sense with the conjugate of $\zeta(x) - p$. It follows similarly that for any simple closed curve C in Z and any point p within C, we have

$$(5) \qquad \frac{1}{2\pi i}\,\mu_{ab}(\zeta, p) = \pm 1 = w(\zeta, p)$$

for any traversal ζ of C. This is shown above in case C is a circle. In case C is a rectangle we have only to replace r in the representation for $\zeta(x) - p$ in the circle case by the length $r(x)$ of the segment joining p to the unique point where the ray $\theta = 2\pi x$ cuts C. These are the only cases to be used below. We define a *positive traversal* of C as any ζ for which we get $+1$ in (5).

Thus it follows that for any continuous complex-valued function $w = f(z)$ defined on a simple closed curve C in Z, all positive traversals of C give the same value of $\mu_{ab}(f\zeta, p)$ for $p \,\varepsilon\, W - f(C)$. Since we therefore can find μ directly from f on C, we write $\mu(f, p)$ instead of $\mu_{ab}(f\zeta, p)$ when the traversal is a positive one. Similarly, we write $w_C(f, p)$ for the winding number of f about p for positive traversals.

We note also that since for any subdivision $a = x_0 < x_1 < x_2 \cdots < x_n = b$ of the interval ab we have $\mu_{ab}(f\zeta, p) = \sum \mu_{x_{j-1}x_j}(f\zeta, p)$, it follows that for any cyclicly ordered finite set $x_0, x_1, x_2, \cdots x_{n-1}, x_n = x_0$ taken on C in the positive sense we have

$$\mu_C(f, p) = \sum \mu_{x_{j-1}x_j}(f, p).$$

Now let $f(z)$ be any mapping from a rectangle C in a complex plane Z to a complex plane W and let R be the interior of C.

(2.2) THEOREM. *If $p \, \varepsilon \, W - f(C)$ and f admits a continuous extension to R into $W - p$ [or if f is given on $C + R$ and $f(C + R)$ does not contain p] then*

$$w_C(f, p) = 0.$$

Proof. Let f be given on or extended to R so that if $E = f(C + R)$ then E does not contain p. Let R be subdivided by lines parallel to its sides into a finite number of rectangles $C_1, C_2, \cdots, C_n$ with interiors $R_1, \cdots, R_n$ respectively and small enough so that for each $k \leq n$,

$$\delta[f(R_k)] < \rho(p, E).$$

Then since p is in the unbounded component of the complement of $f(\bar{R}_k)$ for each k, we have

$$w_{C_k}(f, p) = 0 \qquad \text{for } 1 \leq k \leq n.$$

However, since each side s of a rectangle C_j which is within R appears on exactly two of the rectangles C_{j_1} and C_{j_2} and is traversed in opposite senses when C_{j_1} and C_{j_2} are traversed positively, it follows that the net contribution of the side s to $\sum w_{C_k}(f, p)$ is 0. On the other hand if s is on C it is on just one C_k and its contribution to $w_C(f, p)$ is the same as its contribution to $w_{C_k}(f, p)$. Accordingly we have

$$w_C(f, p) = \sum_1^n w_{C_k}(f, p) = 0.$$

3. Zeros and non-zeros of the derivative.

(3.1) *Let $f(z)$ be continuous in a region R of Z and differentiable at a point z_0 in R. If $f'(z_0) \neq 0$, for any sufficiently small circle or rectangle C enclosing z_0 we have, for $w_0 = f(z_0)$,*

$$w_C(f, w_0) = 1.$$

For we can write

(*) $$f(z) - w_0 = (z - z_0)\,[f'(z_0) - \epsilon(z)]$$

where $\lim\limits_{z \to z_0} \epsilon(z) = 0$. If C is taken sufficiently small it will lie in R and neither side of (*) will vanish on C. Then by (4) above,

$$\mu_C(f, w_0) = \mu_C(z - z_0, 0) + \mu_C[f'(z_0) - \epsilon(z), 0]$$

$$= \mu_C(z, z_0) + \mu_C[-\epsilon(z), -f'(z_0)].$$

The first term on the right is $2\pi i$ by (5) and the second term is zero for C sufficiently small by (1.2), since $\epsilon(C)$ lies in an arbitrarily small neighborhood of 0. Dividing through by $2\pi i$ gives $w_C(f, w_0) = 1$.

We next prove the elementary result:

(3.2) *If a function* $w = f(z)$ *has a derivative of* 0 *at each point of the bounded set* E *in* Z, *then* $f(E)$ *can contain no open set in the* w-*plane.*

For let D be a closed square of side a containing E in its interior. Let $\delta > 0$ be given and define $\epsilon > 0$ so that $\epsilon < 1/2a\sqrt{\delta/2}$. For each $n > 0$ let D_n be the subdivision of D into 4^n equal closed squares. Now for each $z' \,\epsilon\, E$ there exists an $n > 0$ and a set $E_{z'}$ which is the union of 1, 2 or 4 squares of D_n each containing z' and such that z' is interior to $E_{z'}$ and we have

(i) $$\left| f(z) - f(z') \right| < \epsilon \left| z - z' \right|$$

for all $z \,\epsilon\, E_{z'}$.

By the Lindelof Theorem, E is contained in the union of a countable number of these sets $E_{z'}$, say $E \subset \sum E_{z_i'}$. We now arrange all those squares (if any) of D_1 which appear in any of the $(E_{z_i'})$ in a sequence $S_1, S_2, \cdots, S_{n_1}$ intersecting E in $E_1, E_2, \cdots, E_{n_1}$ respectively, letting $z_1, z_2, \cdots, z_{n_1}$ be the corresponding points z_i' in each case so that $z_i \,\epsilon\, E_i$ and $E_i \subset E_{z_i}$. Similarly, all squares of D_2 which appear in any of the $(E_{z_i'})$ but which are not contained in $\sum_1^{n_1} S_i$ are arranged in a sequence $S_{n_1+1}, \cdots, S_{n_2}$ intersecting E in $E_{n_1+1}, \cdots, E_{n_2}$ respectively and the corresponding points $z_{n_1+1}, \cdots, z_{n_2}$ similarly chosen. Next all squares of D_3 appearing in any of the $E_{z_i'}$ but not contained in $\sum_1^{n_2} S_i$ are ordered $S_{n_2+1}, \cdots, S_{n_3}$, and so on indefinitely. Then clearly $E = \sum E_m$ and for each m, $\delta(E_m) \leqq \sqrt{2}$ (side a_m of S_m) or $\delta(E_m)^2 \leqq 2a_m^2$. Thus since the interiors of the S_m are non-overlapping, $\sum a_m^2 \leqq a^2$ so that we have

(ii) $$\sum \delta(E_m)^2 \leqq 2a^2.$$

Now since (i) holds in each E_m for $z' = z_m$, we have

$$\delta[f(E_m)] \leqq 2 \,\text{l.u.b.}_{z \epsilon E_m} \left| f(z) - f(z_m) \right| \leqq 2 \,\epsilon\, \delta(E_m)$$

or,

$$\delta[f(E_m)]^2 \leqq 4\epsilon^2 \delta(E_m)^2.$$

Whence, by (ii)

(iii) $$\sum \delta[f(E_m)]^2 \leqq 4\epsilon^2 \sum \delta(E_m)^2 \leqq 4\epsilon^2 \cdot 2a^2 < \frac{4}{4a^2}\frac{\delta}{2} \cdot 2a^2 = \delta.$$

Now if the set $f(E) = \sum f(E_m)$ contained an open set and thus contained a closed square A, then since each of the sets $f(E_m)$ lies interior to a circle of area $< 2\pi\delta[f(E_m)]^2$, we could cover A by a finite number of these circle interiors the sum of whose areas would be $< 2\pi\delta$. Since δ can be taken as small as we please, in particular $< 1/2\pi$ times the area of A, this clearly is impossible.

4. Index for differentiable functions. Maximum principle.

(4.1) THEOREM. *Let $f(z)$ be continuous inside and on a rectangle C with interior R and differentiable on the inverse of a dense open subset E_0 of $E = f(R + C) - f(C)$. For any $p \, \varepsilon \, E$ we have*

$$w_C(f, p) > 0.$$

Proof. Let Q_0 be the component of E containing p. As Q_0 is open in E, $Q_0 \cdot E_0$ contains a region Q in E and $f^{-1}(Q)$ is open in R. Since there are only countably many components of $f^{-1}(Q)$ whereas Q is an uncountable set, there is at least one component of $f^{-1}(Q)$ on which f is not constant. Hence there is a point z_0 of $f^{-1}(Q)$ where $f'(z_0) \neq 0$, because by the mean value theorem for real functions it follows that if a function $u(x, y)$ has identically vanishing partial derivatives on an open connected set in the plane, it must be constant on this set.

Hence by (3.1) if J is a sufficiently small rectangle about z_0 lying together with its interior I in $f^{-1}(Q)$, we have

$$w_J(f, w_0) = 1$$

where $w_0 = f(z_0)$. Hence by (1.2) w_0 lies in a bounded component D of $W - f(J)$. Thus by (2.2) and (1.1) every point of D must lie in $f(I)$ and hence in Q. Since Q therefore contains an open set in W, by (3.2) Q contains a point q such that $f'(z)$ does not vanish on the set $f^{-1}(q)$. Then $f^{-1}(q)$ must consist of a finite number of points $q_1, q_2, \cdots, q_m$ in R.

Now by (2.2) it follows that there exists a $\delta > 0$ such that if j is any integer, $1 \leq j \leq m$, and G is any rectangle in R of diameter $< \delta$ enclosing q_j, then

(*) $$w_G(f, q) = 1.$$

Now let $R + C$ be subdivided by lines parallel to its sides, none going through any of the points q_j, into a finite number of rectangles $C_1, C_2, \cdots,$ C_n of diameter $< \delta$ and also small enough so that no one of them encloses more than one of the points q_j. The points $q_1, \cdots, q_m$ will then lie, respectively, in the interiors of rectangles $C_{n_1}, C_{n_2}, \cdots, C_{n_m}$ of this set.

Now if C_j is a rectangle of the subdivision not enclosing one of the points q_k, we have

$$w_{C_j}(f, q) = 0.$$

Accordingly, by (*), $\sum_{j=1}^{n} w_{C_j}(f, q) = \sum_{k=1}^{m} w_{C_{n_k}}(f, q) = m$.

On the other hand,

$$\sum_{j=1}^{n} w_{C_j}(f, q) = w_C(f, q),$$

since the contribution of side s of a C_j lying interior to R to the sum on the left is zero as it occurs twice with opposite signs. Thus $w_C(f, q) = m > 0$. Since p and q are both in Q_0, $w_C(f, p) = w_C(f, q) > 0$.

As a direct consequence of (2.2) and (4.1) we get

(4.2) THEOREM. *If $w = f(z)$ is continuous on a rectangle C and on its interior R and is differentiable on the inverse of a dense open subset of $f(R + C) - f(C)$, then $f(R + C)$ consists of $f(C)$ together with certain bounded components of $W - f(C)$.*

This in turn gives at once

(4.3) MAXIMUM PRINCIPLE. *If $\left|f(z)\right| \leq M$ on C, then $\left|f(z)\right| \leq M$ on R. In particular, if $f(z)$ is continuous on a rectangle C and its interior R and differentiable on $R - F$ where F is a finite set of points, then $\left|f(z)\right| \leq M$ on C implies $\left|f(z)\right| \leq M$ on $R + C$.*

Bibliography

AHLFORS, L. V.
[1] *Development of the theory of conformal mapping,* · · · , Contributions
to the Theory of Riemann Surfaces, Princeton University Press, 1953
(Annals of Mathematics Studies, No. 30).

EGGLESTON, H. C.
[1] (with Ursell, H. D.), *On the lightness and strong interiority of analytic
functions,* J. London Math. Soc. 27 (1952), 260–271.

EILENBERG, S.
[1] *Transformations continues en circonference et la topologie du plan,*
Fund. Math. 26 (1936), 61-112.

HEINS, M. H.
[1] (with Morse, M.), *Deformation classes of meromorphic functions and
their extensions to interior transformations,* Acta Math. 79 (1947),
51–103.

JENKINS, J.
[1] (with Morse, M.), *Conjugate nets on an open Riemann surface,* from
Lectures on Functions of a Complex Variable, University of Michigan
Press, 1955.

KERÉKJÁRTÓ, B. v.
[1] Topologie, Berlin, Springer, 1923.

KURATOWSKI, C.
[1] *Homotopie et fonctions analytiques,* Fund. Math. 33 (1945), 316–367.
[2] Topologie II, Warszawa, Polska Akad. Nauk, 1950.

MOORE, R. L.
[1] Foundations of Point Set Theory, New York, 1932 (American Mathematical Society, Colloquium Publications, vol. 13).

MORSE, M.
[1] Topological Methods in the Theory of Functions of a Complex
Variable, Princeton University Press, 1947. (Annals of Mathematics
Studies, No. 15).
[2] See Heins [1].
[3] See Jenkins [1].

NEVANLINNA, R.
[1] Eindeutige Analytische Funktionen, Berlin, Springer, 1936.

PLUNKETT, R. L.
[1]. *A topological proof of a theorem of complex analysis*, Proc. Nat. Acad. Sci., 42 (1956), 425–426.

POLAK, A. I.
[1] *On functions taking no constant value on a non-degenerate connected set*, Dokladi Akad. Nauk, USSR, 100 (1955), 213–215.

STOÏLOW, S.
[1] Principes Topologiques de la Théorie des Fonctions analytiques, Paris, Gauthier-Villars, 1938.
[2] *Sur un théorème topologique*, Fund. Math., 13 (1929), 186–194.

TITUS, C. J.
[1] (with Young, G. S.), *A Jacobian condition for interiority*, Michigan Math. J. 1 (1952), 89–94.

URSELL, H. D.
[1] See Eggleston [1].

WHYBURN, G. T.
[1] *Analytic Topology*, New York, 1942 (American Mathematical Society, Colloquium Publications, vol. 28).
[2] *Introductory topological analysis*, from Lectures on Functions of a Complex Variable, University of Michigan Press, 1955.
[3] *Topological analysis*, Bull. Amer. Math. Soc., 62 (1956), 204–218.
[4] *Open mappings on locally compact spaces*, Amer. Math. Soc. Mem., No. 1, New York, 1950.
[5] *Sequence approximations to interior mappings*, Ann. Soc. Polon. Math., 21 (1948), 147–152.

YOUNG, G. S.
[1] See Titus [1].

Supplement to Bibliography

CONNELL, E.
  On properties of analytic functions, Duke Math. J., 28 (1961), 73–81.
CONNELL, E. and P. PORCELLI
  Power series development without Cauchy's formula, Amer. Math. Soc. Bull., 67 (1961), 177–181.
  An algorithm of J. Shur and the Taylor series, Amer. Math. Soc. Proc., 13 (1962), 232–235.
HEINS, MAURICE
  Interior mappings of an orientable surface into S^2, Amer. Math. Soc. Proc., vol. 2 (1951), 951–952.
McSHANE, E. J., and BOTTS, T. A.
  Real Analysis, D. Van Nostrand Co., Inc., New York, 1959.
PLUNKETT, R. L.
  A topological proof of the continuity of the derivative of a function of a complex variable, Amer. Math. Soc. Bull., 65 (1959), 1–4.
READ, A. H.
  Higher derivatives of analytic functions from the standpoint of topological analysis, J. London Math. Soc., 36 (1961), 345–352.
WHYBURN, G. T.
  Developments in topological analysis, Fund. Math., 50 (1962), 305–318.
  The Cauchy inequality in topological analysis, Proc. Natl. Acad. Sci., 48 (1962), 1335–1336.

Index